GRIEF CHILD

It was midnight. The little village of Susa slept in darkness in the heart of the forest farms, among the tall trees. The mahoganies and sapeles stood tall in the dark sky, providing a canopy over the village and deepening the density of the pitch-dark night.

From a distant cluster of neighbouring villages, Adu heard a dog bark. Another dog howled. In this village midnight was a dangerous time. It was better not to be awake or to hear noises.

Drifting into sleep, Adu was gripped by nightmare. He was in the forest, all alone—overwhelmed by fear—when the leopard sprang...

To be chased by an animal in a dream was a bad omen. Someone was going to die.

In this haunting tale the power of light struggles with the power of darkness to claim the life of Adu, the 'grief child'. Brooding over and infusing all is the West African setting—the living, breathing landscape of forest, farm and village.

LAWRENCE DARMANI was born in the north of Ghana and has worked in both West and East Africa. He has written many stories, in addition to regular articles for magazines and newspapers. He currently edits the Ghana edition of *Step* magazine, and lives in Accra with his wife and baby daughter.

GRIEF CHILD

Lawrence Darmani

A LION PAPERBACK
Oxford · Batavia · Sydney

Published by
Lion Publishing plc
Sandy Lane West, Oxford, England
ISBN 0 7459 1821 2
Lion Publishing Corporation
1705 Hubbard Avenue, Batavia, Illinois 60510, USA
ISBN 0 7459 1821 2
Albatross Books Pty Ltd
PO Box 320, Sutherland, NSW 2232, Australia
ISBN 0 7324 0281 6

First edition 1991

British Library Cataloguing in Publication Data
Darmani, Lawrence
  Grief child.
  I. Title
  823.914 [F]
  ISBN 0 7459 1821 2

Printed and bound in Great Britain
by Cox and Wyman Ltd, Reading

TO
COMFORT,
MY WIFE

PART ONE

1

It was midnight. The little village of Susa slept in darkness in the heart of the forest farms among the tall trees. The mahoganies and sapeles stood tall in the dark sky, providing a canopy over the village and deepening the density of this pitch-black night. The dying moon had done her job earlier on by providing faint light to the children who played in her glow and later listened to stories from their grandmothers. Now, after roaming about in the trees awhile, the moon was far behind the mammoth mountain. The children of Susa snored in their mothers' bosoms.

Adu turned in his bed, coughed slightly, and threw his hands about. He was a child of Susa—the village—and he too had been snoring. When he turned, his right hand fell heavily on his little sister's face. Yaa woke up, frightened. Who had hit her? It was her big brother again. This was one thing she hated about him. Adu didn't know how to sleep. He was always restless in bed and disturbing her own sound sleep. At ten years she felt she was old enough to have her own bed but her Burago, their mother, wouldn't hear of it. She had not only put them in one bed, but had even put the bed in her room. 'You children need watching over,' she told them.

Yaa took the heavy hand from her face and flung it back to its owner. The sudden gesture woke twelve-year-old Adu. He grumbled an insult and stretched full length on his side of the wooden bed which creaked noisily in the silence. As he began to doze again the little village of Susa slept on.

From a distant cluster of neighbouring villages, Adu

heard a dog bark. Another dog howled. He ignored them. In this village, midnight was a dangerous time. It was better not to be awake or to hear noises.

It seemed to Adu that he was moving away from the noises of the night, from the barking dogs, the hooting owls, and the insects. Or were the sounds of the night moving away from him? He couldn't tell. One thing he knew: the night was bad in these parts. Nobody wanted to remember the frightening stories told about Susa. It was better not to know. Yet Adu was a boy who poked his nose into questions that only brave men asked. He knew more about the sadness of Susa and the dangers of the night than other boys of his age. He knew about the woman Susa, the landowner's wife who died; about her ghost who visited the village most nights; about the cheetahs and lions and leopards that roamed only at night, never during the day.

Fear gripped Adu. Where was he? Now he knew that it was he who was moving away from the sounds of the night. The stories of Susa haunted his young mind. He was moving away from the village as if compelled by a force beyond his strength.

He was in the forest, all alone. He looked around, but there was no one. How did he come to be here? he asked himself. But before he had time to think—

'Adu!'

—someone called him.

The voice was coming from that wawa tree in front of him. It sounded like the voice of a woman. Fear overwhelmed him.

'Adu!'

The voice came again. He looked behind him; there was no one.

Suddenly there arose from behind the wawa tree what at first seemed like a dark winding smoke curling up the tree. Then it seemed to become the figure of a long, thin human being peering down at him. He screamed. A deep voice echoed his own voice. He heard a rustle behind him and turned to see. There, strong and alert, stood a giant leopard. The animal snarled at him. Her red eyes scrutinized Adu. When she began to wag her tail Adu knew he was in danger. He took to his heels, but his legs couldn't carry him fast enough. He yelled, but his own voice bounced back to him. The echo this time was deeper. The leopard chased him, gnarling and bellowing.

'Adu!'

He stopped. Who called him? He turned round to see. The leopard stopped, too, and began wagging her tail. Adu was about to take to his heels again when the animal crouched and sprang at him.

Adu cried out and dived to the side of the path. He heard many voices calling him but he couldn't tell where they came from or whose they were. As he swung away from the path the huge animal missed him and fell heavily. She rose up and chased at Adu as he ran through the forest of Susa. Did he not love the plants, the trees and the birds? Why had they now deserted him? For they were now on the side of the pursuing animal. They got in his way and hampered his progress. Susa slept on, while one of the sons of the village struggled alone in the forest with a beast that was determined to destroy him.

Fireflies blurred his vision. He saw people hiding behind trees, but no one came to his aid. He yelled and kicked.

'Adu...Adu...Adu!'

The voices now surrounded him. He felt someone pulling his leg and then his arms. Surely the animal was tearing him limb by limb.

'Papa...Mama...she's killing me...aaaagh!'

'Adu...Adu...wake up...wake up.'

Adu woke up. He leapt from his bed and was about to rush out of the room when his father grabbed him in his strong hands. 'Hey, Adu, look here. What's the matter?'

Adu struggled briefly in his father's arms before he calmed down. Sweat covered his forehead. He breathed heavily and turned his head from side to side as if he was

11

looking for something.

He saw his mother gazing at him in bewilderment. She held Yaa tightly to herself, as if to prevent her from going through a similar experience. Yaa, also confused, looked on. Tears stood in their eyes.

'What is the matter?' his father asked again. He sat him down on the bed, looked straight at him, and asked, 'What did you see?'

Adu looked around before he spoke: 'I saw a leopard...she was running after me...she was going to kill me...' Adu told the story in a broken voice but in great detail. His father Nimo rose up and left the room.

It was daybreak. The darkness that had wrapped Susa round was gone. The sun had replaced the dying moon and was bright over the great mountain. Fireflies no longer roamed the sky; birds now sang in the trees. Adu was confused. One moment everything and everybody was against him. Now he was surrounded by his family, loving and caring.

'It was only a dream, Adu,' his mother said, trying to encourage him. 'You're all right.' But the look on her face said something different; she was scared.

Nimo went into his own room, sat down, and thought for a long time. He didn't like the mention of a leopard in Adu's dream. The leopard was his family totem; a family's totem shouldn't be seeking a family member to kill. Why would a member of his own family be seeking to destroy his son? That was his interpretation of the dream. He was not the kind of man to make a fuss about dreams but he often remembered what his father told him long ago: 'When you dream and see an animal chasing you, don't take that dream lightly. And if that animal is a leopard,' his father had added, 'then you should seek for some help'. It meant that something terrible was about to happen.

Nimo worked as a farmer but he was also a herbalist. Many years before, when this knowledge of herbs was being taught him by his father, he strongly objected to the part that dabbled in spiritism. He was still a young boy then and unable yet to say why he rejected the dealings of the spirit world but he told his father that he didn't think he had the emotional strength to cope with the mysterious practices of juju-men and soothsayers. In vain his father put pressure on him to learn how to consult the dead. Eventually his father had given up, calling him a coward. The other person who had called him a coward was his only sister, Goma, who now lived in Buama, a town west of Susa. Goma said Nimo's rejection of their father's spiritism was a bad omen for their family. From that time she associated every mishap in the family with Nimo's decision.

But why did he remember all this? Why did his son's dream awaken these memories?

'Seek help,' his father had told him. Now what help was he to seek and from whom? What his boy had gone through that morning drove fear into him. For some time he had been unable to wake up the boy, who screamed and threw his hands about as though he was being strangled. That was quite unlike Adu; something dreadful might happen to him, and he must surely look for help. He decided eventually to see a certain young man in the village. Not that he expected too much from Yaro, but, of all the people in Susa, Yaro was the person he felt he must see.

2

Yaro's back and waist ached as he cut the weeds under the young cocoa plants with his machete. But he ignored the ache. The callouses on his palm were hard; they resisted the pain.

He raised his body and allowed the sweat to run down his back. Turning round he tried to measure the amount of work he had done since he came to the farm that morning. About half an acre. Not bad for a lone weeder, he thought.

He had recently been barbered, exposing his protruding forehead which the boys of Susa said contained the words he preached. Yaro himself attributed his skinny physique to a period of raw suffering in his life as a child when he was denied adequate nourishment. People wondered how a man with such red eyes could see properly, yet when anybody wanted a needle threaded, it was Yaro they called, if he was close by. They liked him for his patience. There was not a man in Susa who had undergone so much mockery at the hands of children and women. Yet he never lost his temper. Yaro was a hard-working man and Appiah, his master, bragged about having searched diligently to find such a farm-hand.

The wind blew under the cocoa trees and rattled the dry leaves. The tender branches swayed as the wind rushed through them. Yaro enjoyed the soothing bath of the cool breeze. He loved to see the weeds cut and allowed to dry under the trees. The sight was beautiful to any farmer.

But Yaro's mind was preoccupied. He was thinking about his chat with Nimo the day before. This Nimo surprised him. When Yaro first began to tell the people of Susa about his God it didn't take him long to realize the truth of the saying that a prophet is indeed never welcomed in his own village. This was especially true among the older generation. The majority of them rejected his message. Not even his own master recognized him as anything more than a farmhand.

But Nimo had regard for him. Nimo didn't deplore Yaro's close association with his son. He didn't say Yaro was polluting Adu's mind the way some of the parents did. Nimo took him seriously when he practised his faith. Once in a while he had even expressed his need for the things of God. Until yesterday, Nimo had asked to be prayed for only in passing.

'Are you going to church, Yaro?'

'Yes, Papa Nimo.'

'Pray for us.'

That was as far as Nimo went. Casually. He hadn't expected Nimo so confidently to confide in him or to ask him to pray for his son. When Nimo came to him yesterday and said he had something to discuss, he thought the man only needed help on the farm. But he had asked for something else: 'Pray for my son, Yaro,' Nimo pleaded. 'Pray for your friend; he had a terrible dream this morning. To be chased by an animal in a dream is a bad omen, Yaro, a bad omen. It means that somebody is going to die. Please pray for him.' It was a passionate appeal.

Last night he had spent two hours with Adu, praying for him and reading scripture portions to him. He had already taught Adu to commit the twenty-third Psalm to memory. He knew Adu was too young to understand the details of God's protection 'through the valley of the shadow of death', but he believed: 'Teach a child the way he should go and when he grows he will not depart from it.'

Yaro bent down to continue his work. Smoke from the fire he had made that morning drifted among the trees. He loved to see it. It was like a companion to him. Unconsciously he inhaled deeply the smell of burning wood, and unconsciously his mind took him back home—not to Susa but home in far away Walewale, a town in the north. He was not the only person who had left the dry northern territory for the greener pastures of the south to make a living. No, he wasn't. Susa was full of people like him.

It surprised him how he came to be farming so far away from his home town. The people of Susa said they had never seen a preacher who was also a farmer. Every time anyone said this, Yaro replied, 'Well, now you see one.'

As a boy some thirty years ago he had come into contact with a missionary who went about preaching and distributing clothes and food. Yaro was one of those who received an old pair of trousers. One thing that impressed him about this missionary was his attitude to work. The missionary went with them to their farms and actually helped to uproot some weeds. It was he who had told Yaro that the Bible talked about farmers, corn, trees, birds, rains, almost anything he could think of. And he used these things when he told him a story. Yaro remembered the story of the corn and the weeds. Once a farmer planted corn. In the night some worthless people went and planted weeds among them. When the corn germinated, so did the weeds.

'What did the farmer do?' Yaro remembered asking his missionary friend.

'What would you do, if it was you?' the missionary threw back the question to him in his usual fashion.

'Easy,' Yaro answered, 'just uproot the weeds and leave the corn.' But the farmer in the story didn't do that. Instead, he instructed his labourers to allow the weeds and the corn to grow together, for fear that if the labourers attempted to uproot the weeds they might uproot the corn as well. 'Their fruits,' the missionary told him, 'would determine their fate.' Although the missionary told him that the lesson of the story was that wicked men would eventually be cast away, Yaro applied the story in his own way: if you mix bad things with good ones in your life, the good things will reward you but so will the bad ones.

16

Close by he could hear birds chirping on a heavily fruited tree. Their noise did not disturb the perspiring man. They had been his companions since he came to the farm that morning.

Yaro did not see it, but under the tree where his winged companions rejoiced, there a boy sat. His head was turned and his eyes were fixed upon a long-beaked bird pecking at the ripe fruit. Here was a cunning bird, the young hunter thought. It craned its neck towards the ripe fruit and then pulled one back to its hiding-place. This was a challenge. The boy decided to ambush the bird. He prepared his catapult and waited. The black head came out of hiding. The boy quickly released the stone. The stone hit the bunch of fruit, splattering the ripe ones. The bird yelled a curse and dived away.

Yaro heard the flapping of wings above his head and the wild protests; he knew that someone had disturbed his companions.

'Yaro!'

The voice came from behind; Yaro heard it. He turned round and saw the boy coming towards him through the portion he had cleared.

'Good day, Yaro. You've cleared a large portion.' It was Adu, his friend.

'Hey, look at you, my friend,' Yaro responded, wiping sweat from his brow with his forefinger. 'What are you doing here? You didn't go to school?'

'No. Today...' Adu hesitated. '...I wasn't well today so father told me not to go to school.'

Yaro nodded. 'So what are you doing here?'

'Birds. Shooting birds.' His red-tyre catapult hung over his neck. 'I killed four birds. Look.' He showed the birds to Yaro, grinning.

'You're a good hunter, my friend.' Adu smiled off the compliment. 'Have you eaten anything yet?' Adu shook his head. 'Look there,' Yaro said, 'you'll find some cocoyams. Roast them in the fire over there.'

In many ways Adu was like his father Nimo, Yaro reckoned, glancing over his shoulder to see if the boy was all right by the fire. Of all the boys in Susa, Adu was the only one who listened to his message. The boy had an ear for God's word. He did not shy away as some of his mates did whenever Yaro asked them to accompany him to Buanyo or Dumasi to preach the word.

Now Yaro thought about what Nimo had told him. In the Bible when Joseph dreamt, the dream had a bearing on his later life. Did Adu's dream have anything to do with his life? If so, what was the meaning of a leopard chasing a boy through a dark jungle? Sympathy filled his heart: *God, protect that life; protect that boy from any impending danger.* He prayed in his heart, but he knew he would have to spend more time with the boy and teach him more about sustaining faith.

3

Daybreak at Susa. Adu woke up and quickly sat on the edge of his bed. He rubbed his face and tried to see through the darkness in the room. He could hear some noises in the compound.

Outside rain-water trickled down the corrugated iron roof into many containers. The women had left the containers there in the hope that the rain-clouds that hung menacingly over the little village of Susa would give way to rain during the night.

Adu jumped up with a force that creaked the bed and woke his little sister. He was short—like his father; dark in complexion—like his mother, but with a stubborn little heart with which neither his father nor mother could identify.

He heard his father sharpening his machete in the yard. That was a sign that the day had already broken. It was Saturday and Adu was relieved that there was no school to think about. He looked forward to the activities of the day with his father. He groped for his farm clothes from behind the door, a tattered old school uniform. He opened the door.

'Good morning, Papa,' he greeted his father.

'Did you sleep well?' Nimo responded, as he went on sharpening the machete on the rectangular-shaped stone near his own room.

Adu said he had slept well.

There were ten rooms in that huge compound house built many years ago by the rich land-owner who owned the cocoa and the village.

Nimo and his family occupied half the house—five rooms. One room belonged to him, another to his wife and his two children. The third room was occupied by Mahama, the farm labourer he had hired. The fourth room was used to store foodstuffs and farm implements. Nimo reserved the fifth room for visitors.

All the cocoa farms in Susa belonged to the same wealthy landlord. They called him Yeboah. The man owned a big stretch of land with cocoa, palm and oranges. He did not even live in Susa as he had done some years ago, but came to the village from time to time to visit his farms, to find out if the caretakers were doing the work. Nimo and his household were not the only caretakers in Susa. Almost all the farmers there rented their land.

'Where shall we go this morning, Papa?' Adu loved to engage his father in conversation at the least opportunity.

Nimo raised the machete and felt the sharp end with the tip of his thumb. That was the way to tell if it was sharp enough. It wasn't, so he placed the flat side of the blade against the rough sharpening stone and continued more work on it. Adu knew his father hadn't forgotten his question.

'I thought you knew where we were going, Adu.'

'To the rice farm, Papa?'

'To the rice farm.'

Adu smiled. To the rice farm! He loved it. He loved to go to the rice farm down in the swampy area.

'Sharpen your machete, Adu,' his father instructed. 'Take a bucket, and don't forget the matchbox. Bring the small hoe with you; it's in the store-room.' Nimo spoke slowly as he entered his room. Adu placed his machete on the stone and began to sharpen it.

The door to Mahama's room opened. Adu looked up as his father's labourer, who was more a friend than a labourer to their family, walked out. He was ready for the farm. Mahama placed his thumb on his machete and nodded approvingly. He scarcely ever sharpened it in the morning. Every day, after the day's work, he sharpened his machete. 'It's better to do it in the evening,' Mahama had said to satisfy the inquisitive mind of his master's son, 'so that in the morning I don't spend the day's precious energy sharpening machetes.'

Nimo emerged from his room with his rifle slung over his shoulder. Adu saw it and nodded his approval. Nothing delighted him more than a hunting expedition with his father. He loved to run for the squirrel or antelope when his father had shot it. And if it was an antelope, that was something. He would tell his friends about it and force them to listen to him as he boasted of his father's skill with the gun. And if they thought he was telling a lie he would invite them to go with him one of these days. Or better still, if they would only wait for him outside their house in the evening, he would bring them a piece of the antelope meat his father had killed on the farm that day.

Nimo looked at his boy sharpening away. 'Take care, Adu. The way you handle that machete you will soon be without fingers.'

'I'm careful, Father.'

'Don't forget your little hoe. And make sure that the women come early.' Nimo referred to his little daughter as a woman, though Yaa was only ten years old. Adu didn't like the implication of the last sentence and stood up in protest.

'Father, may I please come with you now? Mother and Yaa will follow later.' Adu's face told Nimo it was too early to disturb the boy's peace. He gave in. 'In that case, gather the items and let's be going.'

The rice farm was two miles away, in a swampy place where most of the farmers in Susa cultivated crops: rice, maize, cassava, plantain, and cocoyam. These were called food crop farms, different from the cocoa farms which grew on the drier land. Some years ago many people believed that those who were meant to be taking care of Ashanti farmers' cocoa farms were the people from the north. They had migrated to the southern regions—not only to extract

21

money from the cocoa business but also to pick and preserve cola-nuts. Cola-nuts, it was said, cost a lot of money in the north. A bag of cola-nuts, people said, cost three times as much money as cocoa itself. It was a more expensive cash crop. Nimo was an Ashanti, but he knew that the work some of his tribesmen had delegated to the people from the north was work he could do himself. He did not feel embarrassed about looking after a fellow Ashanti man's cocoa farm the way some of his tribesmen did. He had left his town, Buama, fifty-five miles away, to live in the small village of Susa. When he had come here fourteen years ago, still a bachelor, he would hear insinuations from all corners: 'Nimo has gone to mix himself up with the northerners.'

What had disturbed him in those days was what people said about the girl he chose to be his wife. Birago's parents had lived in Buama for a very long time. They had come from a foreign land, crossing the borders on foot with other itinerant traders. Birago was born and bred in Buama. She was so used to the way of life of the people in Buama, it was not surprising when she fell in love with one of them.

When the time came for her family to leave Buama, she and Nimo advanced their plans and were married, in spite of harsh criticisms. Nimo blocked his ears against the sneers and insinuations.

At first his decision to live in Susa was derided, but the years that followed told a different story. He ignored the insults and concentrated on his farm. Now he had become the envy of many. He was one of the most influential people in the village, as both a farmer and a herbalist.

Nimo was stout and dark. People who saw him attack the weeds on his cocoa farm with a machete or saw him digging in his maize farm said he was built for farming.

They reached the farm earlier than usual. Despite the rains of the night, the small stream that flowed at the mouth of the swampy area was not as full as Adu had expected. The wooden bridge, a big log that the farmers had managed to place across the stream, was clear above the water level. The last time Adu had been to the farm was a week before; now he stood there gaping at the amount of work his father and Mahama had done. The maize stood erect and the rice was green and dark. Some of the corn was beginning to tassel. The cassava they had planted about a month ago was already competing with the older ones kept from the previous farming season.

The moment they appeared, a thousand birds flew away in fright from the area where the rice was beginning to bear fruit. Some of the yellow birds, apparently daring and not wishing to abandon their booty so soon, perched on trees and palm fronds.

'You see, you see,' Nimo said, 'the birds are already harvesting the rice. You see?'

'Look at them,' Mahama said, pointing his machete in the direction of the birds in the trees.

Suddenly the twenty-acre farm thundered with the flight of the canary birds.

'Just look!' Nimo exclaimed as the birds flew above. 'It's time now to guard this farm from dawn to dusk, otherwise these birds will finish what little rice we have in the farm.'

'Yes, I think so,' Mahama agreed.

The announcement excited Adu. He enjoyed watching the farm from dawn to dusk with Mahama and sometimes with his little sister. It meant coming to the farm before the sun rose and leaving it long after sunset. He liked to watch the red sun gradually sink behind the tops of the trees. And when he went home, about the time the hens were roosting, he felt proud. He felt like a man. He could sit, then, with his father, as Nimo conversed with other neighbours who paid him visits in the evening.

4

The shed was on a mound in the middle of the farm. From there they could see most parts of the farm. Adu arranged the three logs that were already in the fireplace. He stuffed the spaces with broken twigs and dry palm fronds and struck the match. The tiny tongue of blue flame licked the dry pieces and caught the twigs which in turn gradually ate into the dry logs. The smoke snaked into the air, made its way over the rice and maize, circled around in the air currents, and then continued its upward course. Adu followed the smoke with his eyes until it disappeared in a splash of thin threads and dissolved into the nearby forest.

Adu admired his father and Mahama for the good job they had done. Except for about an acre of maize still standing in weeds, the rest of the farm was clean. He was still inhaling his fill of the breeze that swept across the farm when his father called him. Adu turned to see the two men already working hard. He picked up his hoe and walked towards them. He bent close to his father and began to clear the weeds among the tender crops. Nimo allowed the boy to work for some time and then began, 'When you get to the farm...' and Adu could almost tell what would follow, '...your first business, if everything is all right, is to tackle what you came to do before the sun heats the soil and your back begins to ache. You don't stand gazing into the sky.' He paused. Still hoeing, Adu could almost touch the hardness of the words.

'Work, my boy'—it was his father's watchword—'work never kills a man. But a lazy man will die of poverty.' Nimo held a stump in his left hand and cut it with the hoe.

'True,' Mahama responded, hoeing close to his master.

'Did you ever hear of a man who died from doing too much work?' Nimo asked, not expecting an answer. But Mahama responded, 'Never.' Nimo remained silent for some time and then repeated Mahama's word, 'Never. Never, my boy,' he emphasized. 'But ask me if I know a man who ended up in jail because he would never do any work with his hands. Ask me, and I can tell you how many such people I know.'

Adu knew when his father was serious. But what his father had said tickled his ears. If it had been an ordinary conversation he would have wanted to know who had been jailed for stealing. Where did this incident take place? What did he steal? Was he arrested by policemen?

'Even when our mothers used to tell us stories in the evenings,' Nimo resumed his discourse, 'they told us the troubles of the lazy spider. All the time it was the lazy person who suffered, never the hard-working fellow.'

Adu's mind shot to the story his mother had told him and his little sister Yaa, just the other night. His father was right. Of all the stories he had heard and those they read in their school books, none ridiculed a hard-working man.

No—no, Adu remembered—there was one. The story about the Spider and the Tree Squirrel was different. The Tree Squirrel was the hard-working one. He cultivated his own farm and worked hard on it. As for Spider, he roamed about doing nothing the whole season. But when the time for harvesting came he hatched a dubious plan to confiscate Tree Squirrel's groundnut farm. He made a path to the farm.

'What are you doing out there?' Tree Squirrel asked Spider. 'Why are you making a pathway into my farm?'

'Your farm?' Spider retorted. 'What are you talking about?'

The matter reached the elders, according to his mother, and they called Spider and Squirrel to defend their case.

'Elders,' Tree Squirrel began, 'throughout the whole season I have toiled on this land and managed to cultivate some ground-nuts. All the time Spider was playing and drinking with those fellows in the market-place. When the time for harvesting came I went to my farm one day and there was Spider trying to make a pathway through my farm.'

'All right,' the elders said, 'tell us your story, Spider.'

Spider rose up, bowed humbly to the elders and addressed them: 'I know you are all wise people, my fathers. I do not have a long story to tell. There's only one question that I want to put to my friend Squirrel here, and it is this: since the world began, where has it ever been heard that a man made a farm without a path that leads to it?'

Spider sat down at once, an act that increased the weight of his question. The elders began to consult one another. Meanwhile Squirrel rose to his feet and said, 'Everybody knows that I don't dwell on the soil. My home is in the trees. I make my journeys on ropes and branches. I don't need any path to my farm.'

'The elders, full of wisdom, will judge that,' Spider said.

The decision of the elders amused Adu. The farm was confiscated from Squirrel, the hard worker, and given to Spider, the lazy one.

But his father was still talking: 'Whenever you come across a situation where it looks as if a hard-working person has been ridiculed or cheated out of his possessions, look at that situation more carefully.' Adu felt his father was reading his thoughts. 'In that situation,' Nimo continued, 'something dreadful will soon happen to the cheat to reveal the truth.' That struck a chord in Adu's mind. He tried to recall. Did his mother say something bad had happened to Spider in that story?

'Truth,' his father cut short his thoughts, 'does not need support. Truth can stand on its own, although it be suppressed, distorted, or concealed. Do whatever you want, truth will always stand supreme.'

At midday Adu lifted up his eyes towards the way home. What he saw renewed his strength, but he pretended that he hadn't seen them.

Birago, his mother, and Yaa, his little sister, made their

way slowly through the farm, conversing. Their presence attracted the attention of the exhausted farmers. Birago greeted them. The woman knew they were exhausted. She would have readily suggested that they break from their toil but she dared not. A woman should not see that men are tired, and if she is so inquisitive as to see, she shouldn't mention it.

Yaa glanced at her big brother and made a face at him. But Adu pretended that he was not even aware that they were there. Didn't she know he was busy?

As soon as she placed her load in the shed Yaa ran down to the swampy place and was soon lost among the tall maize, her little legs carrying her swiftly. She was going to look for crabs. She heard her mother's caution, to be careful not to hurt herself or break the crops. 'Yes, mother,' she said, and off she went.

Birago watched the three men among the rice digging away the weeds. She was proud of them, especially of her boy Adu. At twelve he already behaved like a grown-up.

Adu had something on his mind that he always wanted to ask his father. He must ask him today. The day's work on the farm was over and the three men were on their way home. Birago and her daughter had already left.

'Father,' Adu said. 'Why do people call our village Susa? Was Susa somebody's name or was it the name of a tree or what?'

The moment he asked that question he became afraid of what answer his father might give him. He had heard the stories. But he hoped his father would tell him that those stories were not true, and relieve his sorrow about the village he liked so much.

When Nimo heard the boy's question he took a deep breath before answering.

The story of Susa was a mystery. The landlord Yeboah had inherited this large area of cocoa farm from his uncle many years ago. It was his uncle who built the village and gave it his own name—Yeboah. The landlord was only a boy at the time the property became his according to their inheritance custom. His mother and some elderly members of his family became custodians of the land until Yeboah grew up. By the time he was thirty he was in full charge of the farmland—and the village. Seventeen years ago he moved from Abenase, his home town, and settled in the village to supervise the work being done on the farms. He did not simply leave the farms to the tenants. He was determined that the land should yield more money, and he found more tenants to join those who were there before he came.

Nimo stopped for a while and then said, 'I came to this village after he had come to take charge. But he married before I did.' Then Nimo laughed. Adu knew something had amused his father. 'I tell you,' Nimo continued, 'Yeboah was a tough man! He's so different now from how he was then.'

Yeboah had married a beautiful young woman from Abenase who he adored. She was the one who tamed her boisterous husband. Until Yeboah married this woman he was ruthless. If a tenant did not handle his farm well Yeboah picked a bone of contention with him. The farmers' respect for Yeboah would have dwindled to nothing if his wife hadn't come to save the situation. She sobered the rich young landlord with her love. She was kind to the farmers. Whenever her husband was harsh with any farmer she intervened, pointing out to him how indispensable these farmers were if this legacy were to benefit the family. She was a woman of grace and Yeboah's deep love for her changed him completely.

Her name was Susa.

Adu was listening with intense interest. He knew that Yeboah later changed the name of the village to Susa, after his wife.

The woman had conceived four years after the marriage, a conception that brought happiness to Yeboah because he feared that his wife might be sterile. When it was time for her to give birth, Yeboah took her to Abenase, their home town.

That was about the time Adu himself was born, his father told him.

When Nimo reached this point he paused for a long time until Adu asked him what the matter was.

'Nothing. Just listen to this, my son, and know for sure that we live in a strange world. Yeboah took his wife home, but the woman never came back to his village.'

Mahama was hearing the story for first time. 'What happened to her?' he asked.

'There was a road accident two months after she gave birth to a baby girl. According to the story, she was coming to the village to visit her husband when the accident occurred. Susa was one of the people who died on the spot. The strange part is that to this day no one knows what happened to the child. The woman's body was found but not her daughter's. Only a few people died. Some of the survivors had dispersed before many people arrived at the scene. Others were carried to the hospital for treatment and were discharged. The baby has never been found till this day.'

Immediately, Adu felt sorry for the landlord, though he did not understand the full impact of Yeboah's loss. Nimo continued, and told him that since the accident the man had never been the same. He had withdrawn into himself and talked less. He changed the name of the village from Yeboah, his own name, to Susa his wife's name. The strong, well-built man grew thin. He was often absent-minded. Usually men did not cry—but Yeboah wept. The people of Susa realized that wealth was not the most important thing on earth. For Yeboah, his wife came first. When he lost her, he lost everything.

It was not until recently that Yeboah had married again. Those who knew Yeboah said the loss of Susa had left an indelible mark on him. Not even the naming of the village after his first wife satisfied the yearning in his heart. His continued stay in the village reminded him of Susa. He wanted to remember her always, but the more he did, the more miserable he became. Finally he left the village and

29

went to live in Abenase.

As Nimo recounted this sad story, a terrifying thought occurred to him. Somehow, every ten years in his own life, something terrible had happened. At the age of fifteen he had slipped and fallen on a hot coalpot. He still had the wounds on his thigh. Then his father had died when he was twenty-five. Ten years later, right here at Susa, a catastrophic bush fire had swept through the land, destroying crops and other plants. And that was now exactly ten years ago.

5

'Father, we've got a visitor,' Adu announced to his father as Nimo returned from the farm one evening.

'Visitor?' he asked the boy, wondering who it could be.

'Yes.'

'From where?'

'From Buama. It's Aunt.'

'Aha!' Nimo said, 'Goma is here! That means she's fine now; I heard she wasn't well.' Nimo said this for Adu's sake but inside he felt a pang of worry. His sister's presence could mean that many unpleasant matters were in store for him. He remembered that the last time she was here, a year ago, they had quarrelled most of the time.

When they went inside the house Nimo was surprised to see the condition of his sister. She looked thinner and darker.

'Ah, so Adu was right. He told me you were here,' Nimo addressed his sister.

'Yes. I came just a while ago,' said the woman. A girl sat beside her. That was Ama, her daughter.

'Look at Ama, she's grown so fast,' Nimo commented. 'She's a big woman already.' The compliment tickled Adu. To his father every girl was already a grown-up woman.

'Welcome, Goma, my sister,' Nimo said in a serious tone. 'What a surprise to see you today!'

'I decided to pay you a surprise visit,' Goma said. 'I was hoping you wouldn't be away.'

'I've not been travelling much these days, my sister. Our farms are taking all our time. This is the time to conquer the weeds before they conquer you.'

31

'I know.'

Mahama came out of his room and walked towards the visitor. 'Welcome,' he greeted Goma.

'That is Mahama, my sister,' Nimo said. 'He joined me about eight months ago to help us on the farms.'

'How are you, Mahama?'

Mahama answered that he was fine except for a minor fever because of the mosquitoes. Goma said it was the season. Even in their home town Buama, some people were down with fever because of mosquitoes.

'I heard you weren't well, my sister,' said Nimo. 'How are you now?'

'Oh, so you heard it?' replied Goma, and immediately Nimo knew a reprimand was on the way. 'Why didn't you come to see me? I almost died, you know?'

'Don't say that, my sister. Death is far away from you.' He was somewhat relieved that Goma didn't throw a jabbing comment at him in the presence of the children and Mahama.

'Where are the women?' Goma asked, casting her eyes about to see if Birago was around.

'Where's your mother, Adu?' Nimo asked. Before Adu could answer, Birago and Yaa entered carrying pans of water, which was dripping down their faces.

'There they come,' Adu replied.

Birago saw Goma and let out a yell of surprise. 'Hey, what a surprise, Goma. You're here. Welcome, welcome!' Birago and Yaa poured their water into the big barrel in the corner of the compound and sat down to greet the visitors.

Adu hid behind his father and looked very carefully at the woman and her daughter as the adults engaged in exchanging information about Buama and Susa. Something about the woman sounded an alarm within him. He tried to locate it by checking various events his father had mentioned to him, but he could not find anything to explain his feelings. His own recollections of her were shallow and uneventful. He had seen her a couple of times but every time she looked closely at him he felt something pulling him away from her. As he watched he could see her scanning the house, but she was doing it as if she didn't want to be noticed doing so.

Goma eyed the kitchen area, then the rough floor of the compound house. She was looking through the open window of the store-room and once in a while lifting up her eyes towards the bags of corn and rice standing near the door.

Adu scrutinized Goma. Her eyes were dark and deeply-set. They were small eyes. Now he understood why she always opened her eyes wide—scaring!—every time she looked up towards the store-room window. Goma was dark, unlike her daughter, and the girl, unlike her mother, looked well-fed. Once in a while, as she talked, Goma would stretch her legs and Adu saw how thin they were. Something was pushing Adu away from the woman. What was it? He tried to spot it. Yes: her eyes. They were red and flashing. Each time she shifted her eyes from one object to another they shone as though they were reflecting an outer light.

Few people in Susa did any serious work on Sundays. They did small jobs like weave a basket or mat, mend a garden fence, tend the garden itself, pluck peppers and dry them, cut firewood, crack palm kernels, or extract palm oil from pounded palm-nuts. Although many usually ended the day exhausted, such duties were still considered light work since they did not involve going to the farm.

Nimo might have gone to his farm, but his sister's presence made him do light work instead.

Unlike Nimo, Adu and his friend Yaro spent their Sunday morning visiting places. At the time Nimo sat down to talk with his sister, Adu and Yaro were already on their way back from one village. The path through the cocoa plantation was well trodden. It meandered through the ageing trees that made a leafy roof above them. Adu, wearing a white short-sleeved shirt and a pair of black shorts, led the way. They were coming from Buanyo, a neighbouring cocoa-growing village just two miles away.

This village was a mission field to Yaro, but Adu found the attitude of the people irritating. They called his friend by all kinds of derogatory names: whiteman's slave, chief celibate, wizard, northerner. They said the reason Yaro was not married was because he was not a man and because he feared women. Thinking about this reminded Adu of an incident. One day he was sitting with his friends outside their house when Yaro came by. His friends waited until he had passed and then Siaka, the timid, said, 'There goes the man who doesn't know what to do with women.'

'What do you mean?' Adu had asked, ready to defend his friend.

'You haven't heard?' Siaka said. 'You haven't heard that Boye's father once sent a woman to sleep in the same room as Yaro when they got a visitor? He did this because he wanted to test him. But the next day the woman told Appiah that Yaro was not a man.'

Of course he had heard that story and he'd even dared to ask Yaro about it.

'Leave them to say what they want, Adu,' Yaro had told him. 'What my master expected me to do was wrong.' And he went on to tell him why.

There were others who said that they did not believe what Yaro came to tell them Sunday after Sunday. 'If God had no wife, how come he had a son?' they asked him often. And why talk about God having only one son when there were so many people in the world? Were they not also sons of God? As for heaven, why, they were all going there. Why would God take some of his children to heaven and burn others in hell?

As Adu recalled this he knew that he himself was as puzzled as those who asked the questions. The thing that bewildered him most was that in spite of this harassment Yaro kept going to Buanyo.

'Didn't I tell you, Adu, those people are open-hearted for the Word of God,' Yaro said, interrupting his friend's thoughts.

'But, Yaro, I thought they are always giving us trouble?'

'The questions they ask are not troubles, Adu. The people who ask questions are the ones who think over the things we tell them. If they don't ask questions, they don't have answers to think about. And those who think about the things get to understand them better, because God gives them understanding.' He paused. Adu was silent, so Yaro continued. 'I fear for those who just keep quiet. It is hard to tell whether such people listen to what I tell them or not.'

Like me, Adu thought. It was true, he had never questioned Yaro about any of the things he had told them, though he certainly did not understand most of them.

'It was necessary that Jesus should ask his own disciples: "And who do you say I am?"' Yaro fell silent. His little discourse seemed to loosen Adu's tongue.

'Is it true that some people will go to hell and others will go to heaven?'

Yaro did not show that he was surprised at his young friend's question. He had told him many things in the past; it would surely take him some time to digest them.

'I normally don't talk much about people going to hell, Adu,' Yaro replied, 'because God does not take anybody to hell: hell was not made for human beings but for the devil and his angels.' Adu remembered that Yaro had told the people of Buanyo this before.

'Heaven is God's home and is meant for everybody. Those who follow God will go to God's home, those who follow Satan will go to Satan's home.'

As Yaro was talking, Adu remembered the people's questions on human suffering and they worried him. He himself had seen how some of his friends in school wore tattered clothes; they were lean and pathetic looking. This season was very favourable, but he had seen some seasons in which the rains failed and people's food-crops dried before they could bear any fruit.

'I don't know why the people were asking about why people suffer,' Adu commented. It was an indirect question, and Yaro knew it.

'It's a real problem, Adu. The world is full of sufferers. Suffering is real. You people here in the south don't know hunger because your land is fertile and even when the rains fail you still have cassava, plantain and all the fruits. Go to the north where I come from. There's only one rainy season—here you have two—and the land is dry most of the year. Hunger—real hunger—my friend, exists in that place.'

'What is your chief food in the north?' Adu asked, feeling sympathetic towards Yaro and his people.

'Millet or maize, but mostly millet. There are also yams, but it is rare food.' When Adu was silent, Yaro added, 'I know of situations when people have killed themselves because they could not find food for their families.'

'Is that so?' Adu was shocked to hear that. The idea that people could kill themselves intrigued him. 'Why do they kill themselves instead of coming to these parts to find food like you and Mahama?'

Yaro thought that was an intelligent question and told Adu so.

'I don't know, my friend,' he continued. 'But there are other people who kill themselves not because of food but because...' Yaro wanted to discontinue the subject; it sounded too involved for a child of Adu's age, but his young friend's mind had been stirred.

'What else would make people kill themselves?'

'Well, perhaps when they feel that their work on this earth is finished.'

Adu thought for some-time and then asked again, 'Who decides whether one's work on earth is finished or not?' That question surprised Yaro.

'God decides. But,' he added quickly, to change the subject, 'God sees the sufferings of people and he helps them.'

The two friends conversed as they arrived at the village. Adu knew that he would never understand some of the things his friend talked about. He said goodbye to Yaro and entered the house. He was hungry. He went towards the kitchen to see if there was something to eat, but the sound of murmured voices from his father's room attracted him, and he went close to the door to listen. His father and his aunt were talking. He wished he could hear what they were talking about. The mystery surrounding this woman was still plaguing him. If only he could hear them talk, perhaps that would enable him to know what the woman thought. An idea occurred to him then, and instead of entering the kitchen he went out again.

6

'Since our father died you've ignored me, did you know that, Nimo?' said the woman. 'You have given all your attention to your wife and your children. You have forgotten me.' They were sitting in Nimo's room; the door was half closed.

'You know this is not true, my sister,' Nimo said, drawing the curtains on the door.

'It is true. Look at the house at home. It is falling apart but you don't seem to care. You don't even know that part of it has already fallen, do you? And yet you're here sleeping in this bush and not concerned about me.'

'The bush is what's keeping me and my family...'

'Yes and I hear the people here are feeding fat on your labours. And I come asking for just a little money to do some trading and you say you don't have money.'

Nimo looked intently at his sister. She was ageing fast. At just forty-two and three years his junior she already looked like a very old woman. Could it be that something was bothering her? Their mother had given birth to only the two of them. She had raised them but died before either of them was old enough to marry. Their father lived and worked in Buama.

'All you do,' Goma was still on at her brother, 'is tell the whole world you have a great wife who supports you! You think it is fair that you should neglect me and concentrate on your own? You have not treated me well, do you know that?'

Nimo was still thinking hard. He knew Goma was right on one point: he had concentrated on his own family and his farming, rather than the family house in Buama.

'You should realize, my sister, that you're better off than me,' Nimo told his sister.

'In which way?'

'You live in the family house which is considered yours so long as things continue like this. But look at me. I'm living in another man's house, just in order to be able to live here and farm. The lands I'm farming belong to the same man. But you're still using the family land at home...'

'Which family land? The family land which is as old as the sun and cannot even grow onions? Why do you think father left it to farm in these parts? Go and see; it's lying there like dead wood. I'm also living on borrowed land.'

'So you see that we're all struggling.'

'Struggling where? You're a man and you look after cocoa farms...'

'Oh my sister! The cocoa farms don't belong to me! I'm only a tenant. Two thirds of all the proceeds go to the landlord. To tell you the truth we're all living on our crop farms.'

Goma was silent. She coughed and spat through the open window. Adu, who was deeply involved in the conversation, looked up when the curtains parted and received it full in the face. He spat out a mouthful of saliva, wiped his face with the back of his palm, grumbled beneath his breath and ran away, hoping that no one saw him.

'I'm sorry,' Goma said, 'who was behind there?' She craned her neck to see, but there was nobody there. She remained standing by the window and looked round the room.

'How is your sewing machine?'

Goma remained silent, as though she hadn't heard her brother speak.

'I see,' she said eventually. 'Is it the sewing-machine which makes you think you've done everything for me? You speak as if you don't know Buama. Is it a place where a person can earn from a sewing machine? Ask me how much I've made out of it since you brought that machine.'

If she only knew, thought Nimo, that he had deprived his own wife of something like that for her sake, she wouldn't now go out of her way to demean his humble gesture. Was it for nothing that he squeezed his own family to buy her a sewing-machine in those days? But he decided to ignore her remark and close the rift that threatened to open. There was something about his sister which he didn't understand. It dated back years. Why did she always find fault with him on very trivial matters? Her remarks about his family were not the sort expected from a sister. When her husband died five years before it was he, Nimo, who provided for her until she was able to stand on her feet again. What had he done against his sister that she bore him such a grudge?

Or could it be, Nimo still searched his mind, that Goma was still brooding over the matter of his herbs and their effects? 'My sister,' he ventured, 'I hope you're not still angry with me about the medicine.'

Goma believed that if a man was guilty his conscience would not leave him alone, and she told her brother so. 'Why do you ask me?' she retorted. 'Who cares about the medicine of a man who can cure other people but cannot do anything for members of his own household?'

'This is where we misunderstand one another, my sister. You know this knowledge of herbs was passed on to me by our father and yet his own sister never had a child. He used to tell us, have you forgotten, long before each of us married, that his herbs could never help a woman bear children...'

'Let's stop this,' Goma insisted. 'The harm has already been done and can never be undone.'

'What harm?'

'I say we should forget this,' Goma almost shouted. Then, as if on second thoughts: 'Despite all this, whenever you have the opportunity you blast me hard.'

'What are you talking about?' Nimo asked.

Goma's temper was rising. 'You know what I'm talking about all right. I'm talking about twelve years ago when, just because of my absence from Buama for three years you called and gave me a piece of your mind. Do you remember how you blasted me?'

'Oh Goma! Why don't you forget this matter? You went away for three years to the north on transfer with your husband. You said your going was so sudden that you couldn't inform me before leaving. For three years I didn't see you. Was it wrong when, on your return, I called to ask about your journey?'

'And what else did you ask about?' Goma shuddered as though she feared the answer.

'What else did I ask about? I only thanked God with you that in those three years you had a baby girl...'

'Now let's stop this matter,' Goma pleaded.

'I don't even know why you're saying all this. It seems like you came here on purpose to quarrel with me.'

Goma didn't say anything. Nimo could not understand why his sister felt so bitter towards him. The rift deepened with every passing year. The more they talked, the deeper the gulf became. Perhaps his sister was right, they should forget it.

When Adu dodged from behind the window he saw his mother standing outside the gate to their house. She was waiting for her friend, Boye's mother, to go with her to the stream. He went to her and asked, 'Mother, why is the woman so angry with Father?'

'Which woman?' Birago pulled her son towards her, pinned the boy to her breast, and picked some bits of leaves from his hair. 'Do you walk on your head, Adu?' she asked. 'Look at your hair.' The boy grumbled his disapproval. 'If you don't walk on your head,' Birago went on, 'you must have starchy hair: it picks up everything that comes its way.' Adu was tickled by that, and he laughed. The sticky substance was the phlegm Goma spat from the window.

'Mother,' Adu asked again, 'why is that woman quarrelling with Father?'

'I said, which woman?'

41

'The visitor.'

'Is it your aunt you're referring to like a stranger? Call her your aunt. Who told you she's quarrelling with your father?'

'But I heard them talking.'

'When?'

'Just now. I was hiding behind there when...' Adu disengaged himself from his mother and placed his hand on the spot of his head where the knock had landed. 'Why, Mother?'

'Never, never eavesdrop on elders when they're talking in private. That's bad manners. Never do that again.' Adu made a stubborn face.

'Shall I tell your father?' Birago threatened. Adu was quiet.

'Don't do that again.' Birago pulled the boy again and continued plucking at his hair.

Quarrelling! Birago now feasted privately on that bit of information. Of course this was an old quarrel and she was fully aware of it. Although her husband tried to hide it from her she knew about the sour relationship between him and his sister.

'What's that big boy doing there? Sucking breast?' It was Boye's mother who came by, balancing a big drum on her head. 'Shame, shame, Adu,' teased the big woman, 'you're sucking breast.'

'I'm not,' Adu protested and ran away before the woman made a big deal out of it in the hearing of his friends.

'Look at him,' Adu's mother said. 'Thrust your breast to these boys and I tell you they'd suck it.'

'As if I don't know,' her friend said as they started to go. 'His friend Boye is worse than him. I wonder what type of boys we have these days who are always tagging after their mothers.' Boye's mother towered above Birago, dark like her husband Appiah, heavily built with hefty thighs. She had equally tough arms. Her water-drum was one of the biggest among their clique of women but she never asked anybody to help her place it on her head at the stream when it was full of water. She could easily lift it from the ground, place it first upon her knee, wipe the dripping water beneath the drum, and then, with a heave, lift the giant drum up on her head without disturbing the headpad. See her pick up her bouncing ten-month-old boy, people said. It was as if the child weighed no more than a leaf.

Birago and Boye's mother were friends. They knew how to snatch a brief moment for their small talks, drop in some gossip here and there, laugh aloud, slap their thighs if the joke was a good one, and then run home to continue their chores.

Someone once asked Boye's mother how they managed to be friends when their husbands were often quarrelling.

'Who said they are quarrelling?' she surprised the inquirer. 'They are the women and we are the men; and like women they enjoy themselves best when they exchange a few words.' Then she added most seriously, 'For your ears only. Let my husband hear this and I'm dead.' The surprised inquirer laughed and went her way. 'Boye's mother! If you follow her, laughter will kill you.'

Her name was Mame-Adjoa, but nobody called her by her name. When her son Boye was still a small child, he had developed an abdominal illness that nearly killed him. The boy's ailment was prolonged and so attracted attention. For a whole year the focus was on Boye. People began to refer to the woman as Boye's mother. The same applied to Appiah, but Appiah told people that his name was more important than his son's: if people could not call his son by his own name, they should not call him by his son's name. Appiah knew how to insist on what he wanted.

Before they passed the last house two women saw Yaa and her cousin, Ama, carrying their firewood on their heads and chatting excitedly.

'Look at the children.' Boye's mother was captured by the scene, 'They're friends already within three days. I wish we still had all our childhood innocence in us, Birago. But when we grow—like the tender young corn—we're stripped of our beautiful childhood personalities.'

Birago replied 'But the adult corn, though dry and ugly, has something better to offer than those tender ones.'

'You're right,' Boye's mother agreed. They laughed, surprising Ama. She remembered a teacher in her school who said that people in the villages enjoyed life more than people in big towns, because the village people were closer to nature and therefore to God. Maybe the teacher was right, Ama thought.

When Adu left his mother, he went directly to the kitchen; he was hungry. But before he could find himself something to eat he heard what sounded like excited voices outside. People were shouting welcome to a new arrival to the village. Adu rushed out of the house. He had hardly gone out when he came in again, announcing, 'It's the landlord, father.'

'Aha!' Nimo responded, coming out of his room. 'What a surprise. The man hasn't been here for months.' Nimo left his sister in the room and went out.

Whenever Yeboah visited Susa everyone was involved. He commanded respect. There was a strong link between the owner of the land and the people who tended it. That was why it was impossible for Yeboah to return home the same day he visited Susa. Once he had tried to go back the same day, saying he was busy, but the people were so eager to keep him that he stayed an extra two days before going home.

'Eh! Who's here?' That was Nimo welcoming Yeboah.

'Yes, I've come,' said Yeboah. 'I know you people are not expecting me now but here I am.' He came in and sat down.

'Welcome, welcome,' Nimo said. 'You've come in good time before the rains get worse and coming to these parts becomes a problem...how's the woman and the children?'

'They're fine. Is everybody fine here? I've just arrived.'

Nimo told him everybody was fine. Most people had finished clearing the weeds in the cocoa plantation. Soon the golden pod, as the farmers called the cocoa, would be ready for harvesting. While the two men exchanged news

44

and information Adu sat by himself in a corner of the house. He knew that soon the land-owner would see him and call him—as he did whenever he came to the village—but until then he had time to study the man afresh, in the light of what his father had told him. As the men talked, once in a while they burst out laughing. But Adu now knew that behind the laughter was a man hurt and grieved. Footsteps coming towards the gate drew his attention. Yaa and Ama walked in, balancing water buckets on their heads. When they had drained the water into the barrel that stood in a corner of the yard they turned to go. That was when Yeboah remembered to ask about the children.

'Come and greet me, my daughters—now where's Adu?' Adu rose and joined Yaa and Ama to shake Yeboah's hand. Yeboah looked at Ama. 'Who is this one? Have I seen you in this house before?'

It was Nimo who answered the question while Yeboah held on to Ama's hand. 'That's Ama, my niece. She's Goma's daughter, you remember—by the way, where is she?' Nimo looked around. 'Where's Goma?'

Adu entered his father's room to see if Goma was there. She was not.

The next morning Nimo went to his sister's room to greet her, only to find her packing.

'What's this, sister? Are you going today?' asked Nimo. He was surprised.

'Yes, I'm going,' Goma replied, without lifting her eyes to look at Nimo.

'I thought you said you were staying for a week. We didn't even finish talking about the reason you came.'

'I don't care.' She continued to pack. Ama looked on helplessly; her face showed that she would have loved to stay a little longer. Adu was really puzzled about his aunt's hasty decision to return to her town. He was told that it was Goma's way. Every time she was in the village and Yeboah came, she left abruptly.

7

Appiah walked briskly. The morning dew was still heavy on the leaves and the tall grass on the path. His trousers were wet right up to his knees. He tried to part the overgrown grass with his machete but only succeeded in slowing his pace. He gave up.

He was a bulky man, tall and slightly bent. His ever-frowning face, along with his extremely dark complexion, gave him a fierce look. Boys in Susa feared him because he never spared anyone who tampered with his belongings.

'The people of Susa are lazy!' Appiah complained as he slogged along the weedy path. 'They will never weed the road—never. They're always waiting for me to cut the grass. It's all right, Appiah will always be around to do it! Lazy people!'

He was returning from his farm in the swampy place and was close to the village. The gourd he carried dangled from his shoulders. As a palm wine tapper he knew how to handle gourds and their contents.

Gratefully Appiah reached the section of the road which had no grass along it. He stamped his feet on the dry leaves to shake off the drops of moisture from his trousers. Then he headed for the tall tree close to the path whose roots formed deep holes. That was his usual hiding-place for the gourd of palm wine. He would leave it there until late afternoon when people returned from their farms, then he would come back and remove it in order to sell it under the shady tree in the middle of the village—the place where the tired farmers retired to relax and talk about their daily work.

He walked towards his home. As he came near the village he decided to visit his garden. He was almost there when he heard a noise coming from his garden. As he approached, he tiptoed. He could see some boys meddling with his fence. 'Look at them!' he murmured to himself as he went stealthily around the garden. He tried to identify the boys. There was Adu, Nimo's son; then Tanko, the fat one whose mother had openly insulted him the other day. The third boy was Siaka, the timid. He saw that they were not in the garden itself but they were close enough to cause damage to his fence. One of the palm branches they were cutting had fallen on the fence. Now he knew what they were about. Although they were outside the fence, they were trying to reach the oranges in the garden. Adu, the son of Nimo, was struggling to pull the stray branch away. As he did, he heard a cracking sound.

'Oho!' one boy exclaimed. 'Take time. If Boye's father meets us here, we're dead.' Boye was Appiah's first son and their friend. He was usually to be found with these other three, but he had told them this morning that his father had saddled him with work at home before going to tap his palm wine, so he couldn't join them.

Appiah looked round for a cane. With a big leap forward he dashed towards the unsuspecting boys.

'Appiah, understand what I'm saying,' Nimo told the man who stood before him. 'I'm not trying to protect my son— no, not at all. In fact, if you want to know, I've disciplined him already. What I'm trying to say is that when you want to discipline a child, do so properly. Discipline him and let him know that you're disciplining him. Don't pin him down on the ground as though you want to kill him.'

Appiah's knees shook; he was angry. 'You are the kind that spoils children,' Appiah shook a finger close to the tip of Nimo's nose. 'Your boy was found stealing oranges from my garden and when I complain to you, you don't want to admit that he is a thief. Is that how to raise children—trying to shield them from being corrected?'

47

Nimo was surprised. Did Appiah really have the guts to threaten him so? He wanted to shout back, but instead he said, 'I'm not saying you shouldn't correct the boy. Do, but do it the right way.'

'What is the right way? Tell me; what's the right way?'

Birago came close to her husband and said, 'It's all right, it's all right.'

'It's not all right,' Appiah shouted. 'I've beaten your boy and I'll whip him again if I catch him near my garden.' He stormed out.

Nimo gaped at Appiah as he walked out.

'Mother, if you see somebody stealing another person's something, is it good to tell the person whose thing is being stolen?'

Birago thought about the question. It was evening and she and her daughter were bent over a large pan of rice, picking it over for stones and grit. Rice was not a staple food, but everybody liked it better than *fufu*—all except the elderly people. Rice, because of its rarity, had assumed a status of its own. The children were always excited when Birago cooked rice, and they often made silly remarks. The question that Yaa asked, however, didn't sound silly and she had to think about it.

Adu was sitting by his mother and sister with a smaller plate of rice, picking over the grains and putting them in a separate container.

When Yaa asked the question, Adu lifted his eyes quickly and glared at her. Yaa knew she had startled her brother and did not care. That was what she was aiming to do.

Birago was conscious of the tension in the air. Yaa might have finished her question with a chuckle, but she could tell that her daughter was hitting at something.

'Who stole anything today?' Birago's concern was heightened. Yaa coughed but her mother did not decode the message. In answer to Yaa's question Birago explained that it all depended on the situation; the circumstance would

48

tell whether it was right to be an informer or not. She promised them a story to explain what she meant later that evening.

Whenever his father and Mahama were not at home Adu preferred to eat alone, except the day they prepared chicken. Then he would loiter around the women's eating-place, hoping for a bone which he could enjoy for its marrow. Adu once sent the whole family into rib-aching laughter by saying that the bone he could not break into pieces with his teeth, few dogs could manage.

After the meal Yaa said, 'Mother, tell us the story you promised us.'

'Let me tell you the story of Tortoise, Rope and Bird,' Birago said. 'Once there lived Tortoise in the forest. She lived under the shade of a big tree in a thick forest. Her neighbour was Rope, and Rope made his home along the big tree. Rope, as you know, is tall and winding. He grew from the bottom of the big tree to the branches...'

'Was Rope male or female?' The questioner was Yaa.

'Rope, like all ropes in the forest, was male,' Birago answered.

'How do people know whether ropes are males or females?' Yaa asked again.

'Yaa!' Adu cut in. 'You've started again. If you don't stop asking unnecessary questions the story will never end.'

'Stories are more interesting when people ask questions, Adu,' Birago said.

'Yes, Mother,' Adu responded, 'but the questions should have something to do with the story.'

'Adu is right, Yaa.'

'All right, let's go on. Now listen, because Rope was tall he could see the foot and branches of the tree at the same time.'

Did Rope have eyes? The question formed in Yaa's mind, but she left it there.

'One day a hunter went to that same forest to hunt. He passed by the tree but he did not see Tortoise. When he went away Bird came and stood on the tree. Bird lived in another part of the forest. As soon as she came she began to sing—you know how birds like singing. Guess what she was singing about.'

'Tell us,' Adu replied.

'She was singing: "I'm Bird, Bird, Bird; I am tall, tall, tall; I travel far, far, far; I have a beautiful house; I have beautiful feathers; beautiful feet. Blue...green...red...gold." As she sang, she flapped her wings together as though she was clapping—which in fact she was.'

Yaa giggled at the gestures her mother made while trying to imitate the bird.

'What type of bird was this?' Adu asked as a point of interest. When his mother told him it was a Weaver bird he nodded. A Weaver could brag that way. It was the most attractive bird in the bush with its multi-coloured feathers. It wove the most delicate nest with a long entrance that pointed downward. And it was the only bird whose nest was stuffed with cotton.

'Tortoise heard Bird singing and became uncomfortable. She told Rope, "Please, Rope, tell Bird up there to stop singing. She's making too much noise and this part of the forest is a quiet place."

'"Why should I tell Bird to stop singing?" Rope asked, "Allow the girl to enjoy herself."

'"You don't understand, Rope," Tortoise pleaded, "if she doesn't stop singing, the hunter who just passed this way will come back and shoot her."

'"And what is that to me?" asked Rope. "Please stop bothering me." But Tortoise tried to reason with him: "If Hunter shoots Bird, she will fall down here. And if she does, the hunter will find me and take me too."

'"Well," Rope retorted, "that is between the two of you. I don't care."

'"You don't care! You don't care!" Tortoise mimicked Rope. "I used to think you were wise. Don't you know that if the hunter gets me and Bird he'll want something to tie us with, and that puts you in danger too?"

'Rope was silent awhile, then, angry that Tortoise had called him a fool, retorted again, "Leave me alone. I don't care what happens."

'Tortoise tried all she could but Rope refused to talk. Then, true to her words, Hunter came by. He heard Bird singing on the tree and shot her. Rope heard the gunshot and did not hear the bird singing any more. He looked up to see if Bird was there but she wasn't. Then he saw an object sail past him. Bird fell close to Tortoise. When Tortoise saw this she made an attempt to walk away, but you know how fast Tortoise is.' She paused to check the effect of the twist in the facts.

'But Mother,' Yaa observed, 'Tortoise is very slow.'

'You're right. Where was I?'

'Bird fell,' Adu replied.

'Before Tortoise could take three steps the hunter was already there. "Heee, look at that," the hunter shouted. "I shot a bird and God has given me a tortoise too." He picked up Tortoise first and then Bird. He looked around, cut Rope with his sharp machete, and tied Bird and Tortoise together.

'This is the end of my story. Whether you like it or not, let this pass and let another come; I leave it on Adu!' That was the usual conclusion of story-telling, and it was Adu's turn to tell a story. But Adu thought this story should not pass yet.

'Tortoise is to blame for her plight and that of Rope,' he commented.

'Why do you say that?' Birago asked, happy at scratching the youngster's brains.

'When Tortoise warned Rope and he refused to listen she should have gone away. If she had gone away the hunter would have found only Bird who would have been easy to carry and wouldn't need Rope to tie her.'

'I agree with you, my boy,' Birago said, 'but beneath the tree was Tortoise's home, where she found safety in the day-time. There was no guarantee of safety anywhere else.'

'Besides,' this was Yaa, 'I think Tortoise was not only concerned with her own safety. She was also concerned with

51

the safety of Bird. If she went away, who would be there to warn Bird of the impending danger? Rope was the unconcerned fellow. He's to blame.'

Birago was surprised at her daughter's reasoning, and smiled proudly.

'Rope is to blame,' Yaa judged.

'Why are you blaming Rope when Bird started the whole trouble?' Adu refused to be beaten.

'Singing,' said Yaa, 'is Bird's way of life and must a bird not sing?' But something was forcing its way into her mind. She tried to recall the question she had asked at the beginning; whether it was right to be an informer. Could this story be her mother's reply? Ought Rope to have informed Bird of the impending danger? She had seen Adu and his friends trying to pluck Appiah's oranges on her way to the incinerator that morning. Should she have warned them? Although she knew they would never have listened to her, at least she would have done something; and wouldn't have felt so guilty when her father and Appiah argued.

8

Nimo took the ripe lemon and cut it in half.

'Hold this,' he said.

Adu took the lemon in his hand. His father poured black powder from a bottle into his cupped left palm. He picked one half of the lemon from Adu's hand, squeezed the warm liquid on the powder and mixed it. Then Nimo took Siaka's left hand in his. Adu and his peers called Siaka timid because he always ran away from fights. Now he had dislocated his arm. The boy yelled at the pain and pulled the hand away.

'Hold him,' Nimo said and the boy's father sat behind him, crossing his legs over the boy's to prevent him from kicking. One of the young men standing by held Siaka's right hand. Siaka began to cry.

Nimo rubbed his right palm with the soft clay and smeared it on the injured place. 'Sorry, my son, I know this is painful, but be a man.' So saying he held the hand and, closing his own eyes as though he felt the pain too, Nimo pulled it gently, turned it left and then right. He pulled it hard and slipped his hand down the injured hand.

Siaka's wail could be heard in the last house in the village. He struggled to free himself but his father held him. 'Keep quiet there,' the man reprimanded his son. 'Next time you will watch a tree carefully when you see one. These flat ears of yours never hear a warning.'

'Talk to him later, my good friend,' Nimo said, pulling the hand. 'You don't scold a person when you're treating him.'

The mother of the boy stood by, tears in her eyes. 'They climb trees like squirrels,' she said, 'and you don't know what it is that they are doing up there. If you knew what these children did they would send you to your grave before you die.'

Adu stumbled behind his father. He looked at the root that ran visibly across the bush path; with two blows he cut it. He pulled it with his left hand and was just about to fling it away when his father said, 'Wait, wait.' The boy paused. 'Let me see. This one is good,' Nimo said and dropped the root into the khaki bag hanging on the boy's shoulder.

The sun had set beyond the trees and the invisible crickets had begun their night calls but father and son had their backs to the way home.

'Roots and leaves or tree bark are good medicine for curing many diseases,' Nimo told the boy.

Preparation of medicinal herbs was Nimo's other 'occupation' beside farming. But it was not like farming because farming brought him income, whereas herbs did not. It could have made him rich but Nimo's own father, who had taught him how to combine leaves and roots to produce herbal medicine, told him never to charge people for the medicine he administered. 'They'll press you to receive their gifts,' Nimo's father had told him years ago, 'but never give in. It's completely free.' According to Nimo's father, that was what his own father had told him. It has come down the generations with that simple order.

All Susa came to Nimo to receive treatment. The government hospital was sixty miles away. Unless an illness persisted, in which case Nimo advised them to go to the government hospital, he offered them herbs—to chew, boil and drink, sniff, bathe in, grind-mix-with-water-and-smear on affected spot. And he did it without charge, just like his father had ordered.

'Father,' Adu interrupted his father's thoughts, 'this afternoon, on our way from school, I showed a friend how to stop blood from oozing out of wounds. I did it the way you showed me when we were in the rice farm the other day.'

'How did you do it?'

'I squeezed...' Adu looked beyond his father and saw someone approaching them. It was Appiah. A long stick of dry wood was on his shoulder. His father stepped aside to give way to Appiah and Adu did the same.

'Welcome, Appiah,' Nimo greeted, adding cheerfully, 'your wife will be happy with the firewood.' Appiah passed by without a word. Father and son continued their journey. Indignation stirred in Adu's heart.

'Continue,' Nimo said.

'But father, why did you greet him?'

'We're not enemies, Adu, are we?' Adu was about to say: 'Father, he insulted you!' But he chose to remain silent instead.

'Appiah is a good man, Adu,' Nimo said, to the silent disagreement of his son. 'You should respect him. Did you see that he was carrying firewood for his wife? Not all men will do that.' Silence. Nimo added, 'In spite of his fits of anger, Adu, I mean it, Appiah is a good man.' Adu did not say anything. He totally disagreed with his father but he kept quiet.

'What were you saying?'

'This afternoon one of my friends hurt himself with a blade. I remembered your medicine. I plucked cassava leaves, ground them in my palm and pressed them on the cut. A few minutes later the bleeding stopped.'

'You did well; but it's not my medicine. It's anybody's.' After a pause he added, 'That is suitable for fresh wounds and not old ones—remember that. Also it's for stopping minor blood flow as I told you before, not necessarily for curing the wound.'

The discussion of Adu's experiment would have ended there but Adu said, 'The boy was so happy that he bought me some sweets.'

Nimo stopped and turned round. 'Haven't I told you never to receive payment when you treat anybody?'

'No, he didn't pay me, father. He only bought some sweets

which he was going to buy anyway, and gave me some.'

'It's the same, my boy. Now listen to me. Never accept payment—in whatever form—for showing somebody how to treat any kind of ailment. Is that clear?'

'Yes, father.'

'My own father—and his father before him—never did that. Other people may receive payment for their herbs and there is nothing wrong with it, provided that their herbs are genuine. But in our family it is for free.'

'Yes.'

'Tomorrow,' Nimo continued, 'when you see your friend, do this: don't let him know that you're paying him back, but buy the same kind of sweets and give it to him.'

'Yes, Father.'

They went to a tree close to the road and peeled off some of the bark. Nimo pulled down a creeping plant along the tree, rolled it into a ball and dropped it in the sack. Adu glanced around to see if a tortoise might be lying beneath the tree. But what he was looking for was only in a story.

A week later Nimo was relaxing in his chair after a heavy day's work when the father of the boy with the dislocation entered. His son, Siaka, followed him. Adu was in Mahama's room when he heard people greeting his father. He came out, followed by Mahama. Siaka was seated close to his father, holding a big red cockerel. Adu squatted near Siaka and whispered into his ear, 'Is this cock for us?' Before the boy had time to reply, his father, after the formalities had passed, said, 'Well, my friend Nimo, the elders say the left hand washes the right and the right washes the left.'

'That is true,' Nimo answered.

'There's no way I can thank you for giving back my son's hand to him. As you can see, he can now use the hand. But,' he took the cock from his son, 'you do not thank a friend with an empty hand. This cock is nothing, my friend. God himself will reward you for me.'

Adu looked on with interest. He wished his father would

56

allow him to respond to this man's gestures.

'We live together as brothers in this village,' Nimo said. 'We should not be paying one another for our friendship. If you pay me for this it means that tomorrow when you show me brotherly kindness I'll be expected to pay you. Take this cock back. I appreciate your response.' Then, to change the subject, he added, 'Have you boiled any eggs for your boy since he recovered?' .

'No,' the man replied.

'Did you kill him a fowl instead?'

'No,' the man said, feeling slightly guilty.

'Ah, my friend. You've deprived your boy of what is due him. You see this cock? Go and kill it for him. He deserves it. Have you forgotten the story about the man who forgot to give his daughter a present when she recovered from a bad disease? The disease returned to the girl. Don't let that happen to Adu's friend.'

That was the end of the gift. Adu was not surprised.

Adu had just returned from school. He had taken a hoe from the store-room and was heading towards his father's small garden behind the house when something attracted him. It was a rather unusual spectacle. At first he felt like laughing, but the groan he heard suggested something serious. He stopped.

Appiah, wearing an anxious face, was carrying his wife on his back, the way a woman would carry her baby. His body was drenched in sweat. The woman's head rested helplessly on his back, and she was moaning like a woman in travail.

For the first time since Appiah had quarrelled with his father on his account Adu felt sympathy for the man. He moved towards the staggering man in a gesture that showed he wanted to be of help.

'Adu, is your father at home?' Appiah asked in desperation.

'No, he's not yet back from the farm. Boye's father, what has happened to Boye's mother?'

'Which farm did your father go to?' Appiah ignored Adu's question.

'The rice farm.'

'Please Adu, good boy, run and call him, I beg you. Tell him that a snake has bitten my wife and she's about to die. Tell him...' Before he had even finished Adu had thrown the hoe away and was flying down the road to the rice farm. He saw Yaro come out of his house and run towards Appiah.

Nimo was digging cassava when he heard someone hooting. He saw Adu cross the wooden bridge and hurdle over the fence. Nimo ran to meet the perspiring boy. 'What is the matter?' he asked, fear rushing through him. Adu was choking with fatigue.

'Papa, Boye's father...Appiah..Boye's mother is dead—dying...' Adu gasped.

'What? Calm down and talk properly. What is the matter?'

'Appiah's wife...Boye's mother. Snake has bitten her and...and she's dying.'

'Who sent you?'

'Boye's father.'

Nimo picked up his machete and began to hurry home. On the way he saw Appiah running towards them.

'Oh, Nimo, my friend, trouble has come home. Please. My wife has been bitten by a cobra and she's lying at home dying. Oh, oh, I'm in trouble today...'

'Be calm, Appiah,' Nimo said.' Run home quickly and cut the place of the bite and press the blood out of it. I'm following you.' Appiah galloped back home.

When Nimo got to the village he saw many people going in and out of Appiah's house. He went straight to his own house. When Adu saw his father he left the crowd to follow him.

'Adu, go back and tell Appiah to send the people away. The woman needs fresh air.'

Adu made his way through the crowd and went straight to Appiah's side. He whispered his father's message and remained standing close to the dying woman. She had stopped moaning now and was lying prostrate on a mat. Blood oozed through a deep cut at the spot where the snake had bitten. He didn't see his father but suddenly the man pushed him aside and squatted near the woman. Appiah pointed to the mark of the bites. Nimo counted the spots.

'Two,' he announced. 'It bit her twice. Let me see the other leg. Did you check there?' Appiah did not answer. Nimo raised the woman's leg and searched. Down at her heel he spotted two tiny blood clots.

'Oh no!' Nimo exclaimed.

'What?' Appiah held the leg and stared at the two dots. He began to shake. He had not realized that the snake had inflicted so many bites upon his wife.

'Send all the people away,' Nimo instructed. He emptied out the bag he had brought with him and chose a razor knife. He cut the spot where he saw the blood clots and pressed it; the woman yelled out in pain. The blood that spilled out was dark and thick. Nimo picked two dried roots from among his things, ground them and pressed them on the cuts. He waited for some time and then told Appiah, 'Leave her to rest awhile.' Then he went out.

9

While the little village of Susa prepared to go to bed, rain-clouds hung menacingly overhead. The surrounding cottages and neighbouring villages, the vast cocoa plantations, the rice farms in the swamps, and the thick tropical rain forests—all were destined to be drenched this night. The pregnant clouds blurred the view to the stars and the half moon.

Birago heard the wind sweeping across the compound, rolling empty cans and shaking the metal drying lines that ran from one end of the roof to the other. She wondered if her snoring daughter had removed all the clothes from the lines. She had asked her to, but when Yaa was sleepy she could not be trusted even to hear instructions, let alone obey them. She must check.

As she opened the door, a cold wind hit her face, blew her cover cloth about and forced the door ajar. She quickly threw the cloth around her waist, banged the door to, and stepped out into the darkness. The wind rushing through the tall trees whirled past her.

She was right. In the flashes of lightning which cut across the bleak sky she could see three cloths still hanging on the lines. A few raindrops fell on her arms and bare back. While she was outside she placed some large cans at the corners of the roof to collect water. Then she hurried back to her room.

The rush of the wind over the tall trees rattled the leaves. It came slashing across the length and breadth of the sleeping village. It was a mighty wind. As she lay listening to the drumming of raindrops on the zinc roof, a sudden brightness lit the openings on the side of the closed door. This was followed almost immediately by a cracking of thunder that filled the silence with a long boom. She heard it pass, crashing into the deep forest, far far away. The rain gathered momentum and was soon pouring down in sheets.

It was the wet season. Rain was life itself to Susa and no farmer would dare raise a finger at the sky for an abundance of rain. Even children knew that to complain about natural phenomena like rainfall was to drive God away.

Birago remembered a legend she had often told her children. God used to be very close to earth, so close that, any time women prepared food, all they needed for meat was to cut a piece of the clouds (which was meat) and prepare food with it. But there came a time when the people complained that the clouds were too close, and hindered the smooth pounding of their *fufu*. They complained so bitterly that God went away from them, hence the clouds were now so far away in the sky.

Birago pulled her cover cloth over her body. When she had the chance to reflect on her family, Birago often thought about the relationship between her husband and Goma his sister. What could possibly be done to right whatever wrong had been committed? To make matters worse, her husband often tried to hide the problem from her. What was there between them that was destroying their relationship? They were the only people left of their family. How could they allow whatever it was to destroy them? Yet she felt sympathetic towards Goma, and towards her husband too.

Birago's thought turned to the rains. This season they had been heavy and long. In the afternoon she had been to the rice farm for some vegetables. She didn't like the way the swampy land was saturated with brown water. The small river they had to cross to get to their farm was running high, very close to the log-bridge. Too much rain could kill the maize, revive the weeds, and make normal everyday life difficult and irritating. But you did not complain—only in your thoughts!

She settled her mind to rest. In the darkness, Yaa stretched her legs and body. She turned under her cover-cloth and yawned. The snoring ceased and so did the restlessness. But Yaa ground her teeth and Birago heard her murmur something under her breath. She ignored it—one of those sleep-talks. But Yaa mumbled again: 'They're coming for us.' It was surely sleep-talk. Birago leaned over and tapped her soothingly. Yaa did not usually talk in her sleep; she simply ground her teeth and snored occasionally.

'They're calling us,' Yaa said again, loud and clear.

'Sleep, sleep,' said Birago. Then she remembered that if a person spoke in his sleep you should wake him and lull him to sleep again. That was what Birago did.

Now Birago herself was feeling sleepy. But as she dozed off she could hear faintly. 'Mother, they're calling you; they say you should come.' This time Birago ignored her daughter.

The torrential downpour soaked the village through and through while Susa slept on. Once in a while a dog could be heard howling faintly, the sound swallowed by the heavy drums and the wind in the forest around. Birago was a light sleeper. An uncomfortable itch reached her foot. She kicked hard and was momentarily awake. She woke to find her daughter still talking: 'Mother, let's go...they're calling us. Shall we go?'

Birago shook her daughter again. 'Yaa, Yaa, sleep, sleep. Keep quiet and sleep.' All went silent again. But Birago had second thoughts. She sat up, reached for the lantern which was burning low and turned up the wick. The room beamed with light. She shook Yaa, raised her into a sitting position on the bed, and tapped her shoulders to wake her. Yaa was jerked awake. When she opened her eyes the strong light hit her and she raised her right hand to cover her face.

'What were you saying, Yaa?'

'Mmm?'

'Who was calling you?'

'What?'

62

Birago studied her daughter's sleepy face keenly. As she stared at her the girl dozed off. Birago put her in her own bed. She lowered the wick and lay beside her daughter. Even grown-ups, she knew, sometimes talked in their sleep. Soon, mother and daughter were snoring.

The morning broke almost suddenly. When Birago opened her eyes, day had already crept into her room. She must have slept heavily; it was very unlike her to sleep till the laziest hen was out of her roost.

'Adu, Adu, Yaa,' she called her children who were fast asleep. 'Wake up, it's day.' The two children woke and simultaneously ran their hands across their faces almost as if they had rehearsed it. As Birago and her children adjusted to the morning, her husband and Mahama were already well into the day. Birago could hear them talking in the compound.

'We should finish that piece of weeding today, Mahama,' Nimo said to his labourer, who was filling the gourd with some of the rain-water in preparation for the farm.

'That piece, I think, is no work at all,' Mahama replied, corking the gourd. Although he had spoken quite naturally, the sentence hung in the air—as if he was trying to please his master. He had spoken without raising his head. Now he did so, to find Nimo gazing up towards the eastern sky. Mahama followed the gaze and realized the sky was blackening behind the trees far away into the forest.

'Rain again?' Mahama's voice betrayed his grumble. He added quickly, to dilute the displeasure, 'It looks as if it will rain.'

'I thought so,' Nimo said, adding, 'but dark clouds towards that side don't bring rain. If it was this side—' he pointed to the north '—yes; but that side—no. If it rains at all, only those beyond the forest will know, not us.'

The two men understood one another—no one wanted it to rain again, but no one dared say that.

Nimo was right; it seemed that even those people beyond

the forest would have no rain. The eastern clouds were beginning to disperse, giving way to the rising sun. What he didn't know, however, was that clouds were journeying hurriedly westward, the birthplace of torrential rains and angry storms. Meanwhile the sun was rising and that was sufficient.

Adu fetched water in the bucket with a conspicuous sluggishness that attracted his father's attention. Nimo was entering his room for his gun when he stopped. 'You're going to be late for school, Adu.' He knew why Adu was behaving like this. Sometimes he wondered whether his son's almost passionate liking for farming activities wasn't because he hated school.

'You know what you must do,' Nimo said as he entered his room. 'You must do it well and do it in time.' Adu understood what his father was saying very well. It was not the only time his father had caught him at his tricks. He had hoped to stay away from school in order to follow them to the farm later on, but now he was defeated before his plans could hatch. To school then he must go.

Any time Nimo was forced to talk or think about school, an old issue surfaced concerning his daughter Yaa. Somehow he had never felt compelled to send her to school. Only once had his wife discussed the matter with him but she was prepared for his convictions about not sending a girl to school. In all Susa, only one man sent his daughter to school, and the latest news seemed to indicate that even he was thinking of withdrawing her. Anyway, Yaa herself had never liked the idea. She was already past the age for starting school and the idea had almost gone out their minds. Yaa was close to her mother and loved the farm work and household chores. Nothing to worry about, then, Nimo thought. That was his usual way of dismissing his conscience on his daughter's schooling. Although he didn't quite like it, he felt helpless.

It was the season for clearing the remaining weeds from under his cocoa farm before plucking time. Nimo was usually one of the first people in Susa to finish clearing the bush. Early clearing made the cocoa yield big pods, but the disadvantage was that the weeds grew again before plucking time. And there was nothing as irritating as plucking cocoa on a weedy farm.

The sun was already above the trees when Nimo and Mahama got to the farm. The dampness all around could kill the enthusiasm of even the most seasoned farmer. It took Mahama longer than usual to get smoke to curl out of the dry sticks he managed to find. Whatever the case, fire must be kept burning; smoke must be made to roam about among the trees; it was the symbol of life, of encouragement and of strength. The women would later bring food, but food brought by women to the farmers on the farm usually did not taste as homely as the food the farmers themselves managed to prepare on the farm: cocoyam, cassava, wild yam or plantain. That was why Mahama, or even Nimo himself, never failed to dig under the old, brownish cocoyam plants to see if they bore young ones. The smell of smoke strangely pepped up the farmers as they attacked the remaining area of weeds that Nimo had talked about that morning.

Back at home, Birago and her daughter were getting ready to go to the farm. Usually they wouldn't follow the men until the sun was almost directly overhead. But today they didn't have to go for water from the stream because of last night's rain.

Birago felt funny. She watched Yaa sticking firewood into the three-stoned fireplace to set the fire. She felt no enthusiasm for doing anything. She sat by the door and rested her head on her hand. She remembered it was a bad posture and quickly changed it. She tried to recollect something, but her mind was blocked. She tried, but failed. She gave up. Then she entered her room and sat still on her bed.

'Why do I feel like this?' she asked herself. 'Am I getting

sick?' She rose up again and went out into the compound, where Yaa was struggling with the fire.

'Mother, the fire is ready,' Yaa announced when she saw her mother.

'Put water in the pot and place it on the fire. Peel some of the yams.' Birago pulled up a stool and sat on it. As soon as she was seated she saw her daughter's dishevelled hair and something about it caught her attention. What was it?

Then gradually her mind began to sort itself out. First she remembered Yaa's sleep-talk the night before. Oh, she thought, it was useless to ask her. Even if she were to ask her about it, she knew instinctively that Yaa would not remember a thing. Birago was about to give up when she remembered something else. She had had a dream. She had tried in vain to recollect it. Now it began to unravel. It was Yaa's unkempt hair she saw in the dream. Someone was trying to pull the girl's hair—no, hands, at first. She pulled her daughter to herself and tried to shield her from the intruder.

At first it seemed like a play, but the woman whose face Birago couldn't quite remember now, became serious and reached out violently for the girl's hair. Yaa had screamed. The faceless woman let go the girl's hair but, to Birago's astonishment, she had plucked off a handful already. From where she sat Birago pictured Yaa's dishevelled hair. But before long she was picturing Yaa's hair in the hands of the faceless woman. Now the woman moved towards Birago herself. The dream was vivid. As she sat remembering, Birago's eyes shifted from her daughter's hair and were now fixed sightlessly on the entrance to the house. In her mind she could see herself struggling to run from the faceless one but the woman overpowered her. The woman had shot her hands straight into Birago's hair and before she could give the assailant a slap she was gone with hair in each hand towards the gate.

A strange cold rushed through Birago and she shivered. With her eyes still fixed on the entrance, she closed them tightly to ward off that near-evil mind-play of the dream. When she opened her eyes again a figure appeared at the entrance of the house. Birago screamed in fright and surprise. Boye's mother, about to enter with into a hilarious greeting upon seeing her friend, stopped short and remained there, standing. Yaa turned quickly towards her mother, dropped the yam involuntarily, and rushed to her side.

'Why, Mother?' Yaa asked. She followed her mother's gaze towards the gate and was the more surprised to see Boye's mother. For a brief, weird moment nobody knew what to do. Boye's mother's face spelt bewilderment. She stood still, wondering whether to retreat or go forward. But Birago broke the spell. 'Ah, look at that,' she said with a long laugh, trying to make light of the situation. 'I was just about to come and see you—and now you're here, Boye's mother. You've not come for us to go for water, I suppose? It rained last night as though the sky was punctured...' It was an attempt to cover up the unpleasant moment.

It worked. Boye's mother, apparently unable to explain the fearful yell and unable to connect it with Birago of all people, forgot about the confusion. She walked to her friend, bursting out in the vigorous way that was her nature. She pulled up a chair and sat down. As she talked, the heavy flesh on her arm shook. She hadn't come to stay for long, the big one said. 'I'm just returning from having dumped some rubbish and thought to pass by and greet my friend.'

Yaa went back to her cooking. She was sure that her mother had yelled in fright, and that her way of welcoming Boye's mother was only a cover up. She stored it in her heart to ask her at an opportune time.

10

The sun was appearing and disappearing behind the clouds when Birago and her daughter left home for the farm.

'Hurry, Yaa,' Birago told her daughter, 'we need to go and get firewood after your father and Mahama have eaten.'

'Yes, Mother,' Yaa replied absent-mindedly, leading her mother through the cocoa trees. Her mother had interrupted her thoughts. She was thinking about the incident at home. Why had her mother screamed the way she did? That scream, to her best remembrance, had a streak of fear in it, yet she had never seen or heard her mother show fear. And her scream had coincided with the sudden appearance of Boye's mother. She wanted to ask her mother why she screamed on seeing her friend. Was anything the matter?

Unknown to Yaa, Birago was occupied with her own thoughts. And they were about Yaa. She tried to reconcile her dream, which she fully recalled now, with Yaa's sleep-talk. Who did Yaa see in her sleep? Who was it who called her? The impulse to ask her was strong, but again she knew there was no way Yaa could remember. It was only sleep-talk. But on second thoughts she decided to try.

'You...'

'You...'

Coincidence. Mother and daughter spoke at the same time.

'What were you going to say?' Birago asked her daughter. Yaa didn't hesitate.

'You scared me, Mother.'

'Scared you?'

'Yes—when you screamed at home. I thought something was happening to you.'

Birago laughed. Yaa laughed too. Birago's prolonged laughter dispelled the fear from her daughter. It also prepared Yaa for the casual reply that followed. 'It was nothing, my daughter. It was nothing.' They walked in silence for some time. Birago's feeling of unease, which had lessened while she talked with Boye's mother and got ready for the farm, began to work its way back. Deep silence fell upon Birago, as if she might refrain from talking for a long time. The rapid heartbeats which had seized her as she struggled with the imaginary faceless woman were with her again.

Birago pulled herself together as best she could and tried to talk to her daughter about general things loudly and at length. Yaa could sense something unusual in her mother's sudden boisterous conversation and laughter, especially in contrast to her previous silence. But she was proud that she could make her mother look so happy.

It was Mahama who first heard the laughter sailing on the gentle wind that swept through the cocoa plantation. He wiped sweat from his brow and glanced back on the portion they had cleared so far. 'A good farmer,' he said, recalling one of Nimo's farm quotes, 'never takes delight in what he has done until the work is done.' Mahama never quite followed that. He stole another glance. From the direction of home he saw Birago and Yaa approaching. The girl was carrying the pan in which was their food.

When the men broke from their labours and settled down to eat, it was Yaa who was more vocal than her mother. What a big area her father and Mahama had cleared since morning. Had they located some wild yam tendrils which she could dig? How about cocoyams? Would she and her mother carry plantain home today? How come the weeds they cleared only four days ago were shooting out so quickly? Why did her father say in two weeks' time they would be plucking cocoa when they look so green? And could she please use

Mahama's sharp machete to cut that firewood out there?

'No, Yaa, you'll cut yourself with it,' Mahama objected.

'I'll be careful,' Yaa pleaded.

'No, the machete will go blunt. Which firewood are you talking about?'

'That one there,' Yaa pointed to a cocoa tree which appeared to be dry.

'Who told you it is dry?' Mahama almost shouted. 'Can't you see the green leaves up there?'

Yaa made a face to herself in defeat. What she really wanted the machete for was to dig wild yams, but now she gave up the idea. She engaged Mahama in other matters.

While they talked, Nimo became aware of the conspicuous silence of his wife. He turned to look at her and didn't like what he saw. Birago was sitting on a piece of wood, head in hand and wearing a strange and melancholy expression. The man was surprised. He surveyed his wife for some time, thinking it was a passing mood. But Birago continued in the unbecoming posture for as long as Yaa and Mahama wrangled on various matters.

'Is anything worrying you?' Nimo asked, looking directly at his wife. The suddenness of the question jerked Birago into alertness and stopped the conversation between Yaa and Mahama. Yaa gazed at her mother. Mahama looked first at Nimo and then at Birago.

'It's nothing,' Birago answered and got up. 'We don't have firewood at home. I thought we should look for some now.' It was true they needed firewood at home, but neither Nimo nor Mahama could reconcile her reply with the reason for the question.

A sudden fear began to surge through Yaa. She stared at her mother for a long time—there was something strange about her.

'I think we should go now, Yaa,' Birago said, picking the basket she brought from home. 'It may rain again and we need to get some firewood.'

'Is your head aching again?' Nimo asked his wife who, in

spite of her attempts to conceal the sad mood, still betrayed uncontrollable traces of it.

'Just a little headache. I'll be all right,' Birago said and began to go. Her daughter followed.

Birago's feelings were changeable and so she was quite right. By the time they were halfway through their quest for firewood she was fine. They roamed far into the wood, farther and farther, several farms away from her husband's. Mother and daughter were soon engrossed in their work. They did not see the changes in the weather. And later, when Birago lifted her eyes towards the west and saw the darkening sky she took it lightly. It was the wet season and such sudden changes in the weather were to be expected. Nevertheless she hurried up her daughter. They gathered the sticks they had cut and bound them ready to leave for home.

'We must hurry before this rain gets us,' Birago told her daughter. As they got ready to go, the trees, plants and shrubs swayed vigorously under the power of the stormy wind that swept across the farm. Even the dry leaves on the overshadowing cocoa trees rose after the hurrying winds. Though it was late afternoon, darkness spread into the woods.

'Hurry, Yaa, hurry,' Birago gasped, almost running after her daughter, who trotted ahead with her own load of firewood.

'It's raining already, Mother,' Yaa said, stretching her arm for more of the raindrops.

'It's going to be heavy rain. I hope your father and Mahama are hurrying home too.'

It was a storm, of the type the farmers dreaded. After such a storm, farmers would rush to their farms in the swamp to see if any corn plant was still standing. Those who had cocoa farms would go to see how many cocoa trees had fallen, or if any of the tall trees had been uprooted to destroy large parts of the precious plants.

But even more dreadful was to be caught in a storm like this while on the farm. Farmers knew that storm by name.

71

They would stop all work in the farm and rush home if they knew it was the one. That was why Birago hoped that her husband and Mahama were hastening home.

The storm was mad today. Birago hurried to catch up with her daughter, who was a little way ahead of her. Just as she caught up with Yaa, she heard the loud chilling sound of a snap. This was followed by the cracking sound of a breaking branch above her.

'Yaa!' Birago shouted when she knew what it was. The branch of a tall tree by the path had broken in the power of the flying wind. Yaa stopped and Birago ran into her. Before they knew what was happening the huge bough crashed down on them, crushing mother and daughter. They both screamed and each heard the scream of the other. The wind carried the sound of the two screams, mingled it with the whistling of the storm, and scattered it into the woods.

When Nimo dashed into the house dripping rain-water with Mahama trudging after him, the first place he glanced towards was the kitchen. He expected to see his wife and daughter but they were not there. He looked round and saw that the pepper his wife must have left drying in the weak sun was now drenched with water. Impulsively he bent down and lifted the basket and its contents into the kitchen. Mahama, who was on his way to his room, looked round and saw some clothes on the drying line. Quickly he gathered them and rushed to the shed where Nimo was wiping streaks of water from his face.

'I knew it was going to be heavy rain,' Nimo said.

'It is.'

Nimo left the shed and entered the kitchen again. There was no sign of his wife and daughter. There was no freshly cut firewood to indicate that they were home. He walked through the rain towards his wife's room. The door was locked. He went back to the shed where Mahama, suddenly realizing that Birago and Yaa were not at home, wore a confused face more gloomy than his master's.

'They're not home yet?' Mahama asked.

'It seems not.'

They sat down. Nimo's eyes were fixed on the entrance of the house, expecting Birago and Yaa to rush in, wet but grateful. Through the door he could see people rushing past to their own houses. Three times within a short while Nimo got up and sat down again. He was clearly impatient.

'Sometimes Birago behaves like a child.' Nimo burst out his distress. 'How can she remain on the farm in this rain?'

'Maybe they're waiting for the rain to pass.'

'Waiting where?'

But worry soon replaced impatience and fear took over from worry. Unable to hold on any longer Nimo took his machete and told Mahama, 'We can't just sit down like this, Mahama.'

They went along the path towards the farm. Although the storm was beginning to abate, it was still raining hard enough to warrant staying at home. The situation was grave. Nimo and Mahama searched through their farm, hoping that the woman and her daughter had returned there to wait for the storm to subside. They were still searching the surrounding farms when the rain began to slacken to a drizzle.

'Maybe they've reached home now,' Mahama suggested. They went for a second time, and entered the kitchen. No one was at home. The two men looked at each other. The look on Nimo's face alarmed Mahama.

'Mahama,' Nimo said, 'this is becoming serious. Where are they?' Mahama saw Nimo's anxious face staring at him. He had no answer. He looked away. Without a word Nimo rushed out again. Mahama followed. Nimo took the pathway towards the woods. Mahama followed. Suddenly Nimo stopped. He turned round and started trotting back to the village. 'Come, let's inform people,' he shouted to Mahama in a broken voice.

Appiah was at home when Nimo burst in followed by Mahama. He rose to his feet. 'What's the matter?'

'Birago and Yaa left us at the farm to go and look for firewood long before the storm. They are still not back.' Nimo paused for breath. His eyes were red, and Appiah saw them and felt the gravity of the situation. For a brief moment no one spoke. Then Mahama said, 'We went back to the farm to check but they were not there.' Nimo turned to the door and hurried out as suddenly as they had entered. Mahama followed. Appiah took his machete and was on his way after them when his wife appeared from the kitchen.

'What's going on?' she asked her husband.

'They can't find Birago and her daughter,' Appiah said, and was gone before Boye's mother could ask another question.

Yaro, who heard everything from his room, came out with a machete and followed the men. Six men from Susa were out on the farms in a desperate search for Birago and Yaa. They scattered in twos, hardly knowing where to head, but as urgently as they could. They did not have to go far.

Mahama and Appiah paired up. They took the path which Birago and Yaa would have taken to reach home. It was Mahama who saw the fallen bough and went to look.

He screamed at what he saw. He yelled so loudly that other members of the search party close by heard him and rushed towards the sound. Appiah was the first to reach him.

'Oh God! Oh God!' he moaned. Other searchers rushed to the scene. Quickly they began to lift the huge branch. From the adjoining bush the rest of the search party came running, among them Nimo. Appiah met him halfway and tried to bar him from the scene. But Nimo freed himself to look.

The sight that met his eyes brought him sprawling to the ground. He fainted.

Adu ran ahead of his friends. They were on their way home from school. The two-mile walk from the town school to Susa was on some days an opportunity for the boys to play, fight, or shoot at birds. Other days it was simple boredom, especially when it rained—like today. They were all rushing to get home. Their feet were muddy and their uniforms wet.

'Rains are good only when they come before we go to school, not when we're already there.' That was Boye, who hated school as much as Adu did.

'As for me, I'm hungry,' Adu replied. 'I lost the money my mother gave me this morning. There was a hole in my pocket.'

'Carelessness!' Siaka the timid pointed out. 'If your mother gives you money and you don't want it, give it to me instead of throwing it away.' It was a joke, but Adu was annoyed. He stopped and waited for Siaka. Between them was Boye.

'Get going, Adu, he was only joking,' Boye said. Adu was still looking angrily at Siaka. The other boys were closing in on them. Boye got hold of Adu and pulled him along, determined to prevent a fight.

'You'll see,' Adu threatened the boy, yielding to the force of Boye's pull. No one talked after that.

In the silence that ensued Boye was the first to hear the sound of many voices coming from the direction of the village.

'What's that?' he asked and stopped to listen.

'What?' Adu stopped and strained his ears.

The wailing that rose with the wind came sailing over to them. It rose and fell, but when it rose again it was clear. The boys knew that it was no ordinary noise. The sound of moaning, crying and wailing came clearly in the wind. Fear gripped them.

'Let's run,' Adu said, and ran ahead of the others. All the boys ran as fast as they could until they reached the village, breathless.

The whole village was wailing. Adu blinked his eyes. He saw many people flocking in and out of his house with hands upon their heads. He remained rooted where he was, afraid to move. At that point Boye's mother, her hands upon her head, emerged from the house wailing. When she saw Adu approaching, she ran and lifted the boy upon her shoulders and took him to her own house. Thereupon Adu started crying. It was obvious to him that someone was dead. Boye's mother placed him down and stared at him with tear-filled eyes.

'Adu, oh Adu, my son.' The woman drew the shaking boy to herself and cried. Adu disengaged himself and wiped his nose.

'Boye's mother, what has happened? Is somebody dead?'

Before the woman knew how to answer that question, Mahama appeared at the door. Adu saw him and the sight frightened him.

'His father wants him,' Mahama spoke to the woman. That bit of information cleared some of Adu's gruesome imaginings. At least his father was alive. But as he made his way through the people at the door, he knew something dreadful had happened. Some of the people who had stopped crying began all over again when they saw Adu. Mahama led him to his father's room.

Nimo took his boy in his bosom and wept so unashamedly that Mahama turned away in tears. He had never seen his master show such emotion so openly. It was a pathetic sight. Adu himself was crying uncontrollably.

'Father, where's mother?' Adu's question was heard by people outside the room and by their response he knew now without doubt that his mother was dead. When he had set off for school that morning his mother was alive. What had happened? For an answer Mahama was made to lead him to his mother's room. Adu prepared himself to see his dead mother and expected to find Yaa weeping beside her. He was not at all prepared for what he saw. Lying on the bed and covered with blankets were two bodies.

Adu lifted his eyes to Mahama and asked, 'Who is lying by Mother?'

Mahama took him back to his father, and at last he was told that his mother and sister had perished beneath the fallen tree. Adu fell on his father and cried aloud, his body shaking violently in his father's arms.

11

Nimo sat on an armchair in his room. The black cloth he wore was gathered around his waist leaving his chest bare. He had grown darker and his shoulder-blade moved conspicuously with every gesture he made. His ribs showed beneath the flesh. As he gazed at the door, the curtain parted and Adu entered. He saw his father's red eyes and looked away. He took a stool from the corner of the room and sat down.

In the room were Goma and her daughter Ama. Nimo had sent her a message about the deaths and they arrived a week after the message reached them. The burial had already taken place.

From where he sat, Adu looked at his aunt. Since she had come he had had only conversations with her. It seemed to him that the woman hadn't changed much since she last visited them. While Adu was watching Goma, Ama was watching his father. Since Ama came she had often been found weeping. Her cousin and friend Yaa was no more.

For a long time no one talked. But presently Nimo said, 'Adu, why not converse with your cousin Ama outside. I'm sure you haven't had much time together.' The message was clear. Adu and Ama went out together. Even after they had gone it was some time before Nimo could talk again.

'It took you so long to come, my sister,' Nimo said. Goma was silent for some time. 'Yes,' she answered. 'I wanted to come as quickly as I could but I just was unable to.' Then she added, 'Looks like your people here did everything for you.'

Nimo nodded. 'They're very kind,' he said.

'I'm thinking of going back next week, Nimo. You're strong—and Adu also. You've overcome this so soon. If you'll permit me, maybe Ama and I should be going back next week.'

Nimo bit his lips and forced back the tears.

'Is there something that I can do?' Goma asked. But Nimo simply gazed at her, shaking his head slightly. 'Can we go back next week then?'

'I wish you could stay longer, my sister, but since you say you want to go, that is fine.' Silence fell between them again. 'After all this is settled, Adu and I will come home to Buama and spend a few days. We shall come to greet our people and bring them thanks for their sympathy and help.'

Goma nodded.

When she left the room someone else knocked on the door and entered. Nimo looked up. It was Yaro. Nimo pointed to a chair.

'Papa Nimo,' Yaro said, after he had sat down for a while, 'God understands all this. No human being can say he knows why this happened to us. And, since God understands, he's taking care of everything.'

Nimo nodded. 'Didn't I tell you sometime ago,' he said, 'that Adu's dream had something in it?'

'You said it, Papa Nimo,' Yaro seized the opportunity, 'But we have nothing to fear if we trust in God's protection.'

Nimo nodded. Yaro added cautiously, 'And this reminds us that while we are still on this earth we should think about the life after death and prepare for it, because life here is for a short time. Knowing Christ and obeying him prepares us for a better life.'

'I know,' said Nimo.

Yaro's words were few, but they were helping Nimo to think about life rather than death.

It was a month after the double burial and funeral. The death of Birago and her daughter was considered a tragedy by all Susa. Over many years Nimo had saved several lives in

78

that village. He was generous and healed people without charge. Why should he suffer a tragedy like this? Why did he lose both his wife and daughter at once? Why was it not one or the other?

These thoughts flowed through the mind of a woman as she made her way alone to the stream. Boye's mother was thinking about her life with the woman who had been her best friend but who had now become part of the soil she walked on.

A man walked towards Susa with a gourd containing palm wine hanging from his shoulders. He also was thinking about the events of the past month. In his mind's eye he saw the two figures trapped under the bough of the tree. What a painful death it must have been! He thought about Nimo and momentarily felt ashamed for the many times he had quarrelled with him over petty things. In spite of his behaviour Nimo had always forgiven him and made friends. It was Nimo who had saved his wife from death. Appiah wiped a tear from his eyes.

Adu sat in Yaro's room. He pictured the two red mounds beneath which lay his mother and sister. Why did it have to be the two of them together? Why did the branch have to break at the very moment they passed under it? When the branch was breaking up in the tree, why didn't some supernatural force prevent it from falling upon his mother and sister?

'Why didn't God, whom you say is greater than Satan, save my mother and my sister?' Adu asked the question again. Since the day of the accident, Yaro and his friend Adu were often together. Their friendship was on a level where they could talk freely, even on matters that adults would not discuss openly.

He had refrained from stuffing the grieving boy with quotes from his holy book, and he had not preached to him. He had simply allowed the boy to pour out his heart. Times without number Adu had cried for hours in the presence of his friend. Today Yaro decided he would open up the subject.

'Adu, the things that you have seen and heard, not many boys of your age have seen or heard. Do you agree with me?' Adu hesitated and then nodded.

'That's why I've been talking to you in a way I never talk to other boys.' Yaro paused to allow Adu to wipe the tears that were now drying. 'Listen to me, Adu. I've told you this before. Death, painful as it is, is not a barrier to knowing God's goodness. God can show you and me how good he is whether there is death or not.'

Adu stared at his friend. Yaro could see that either he didn't understand or he didn't believe. He tried again. 'How people die, why they die, and why some die before others, Adu, we don't understand. But one thing we know is that God is kind and he always loves us.' Adu still wore the flat face that said, I wish I knew what you were talking about.

'I myself don't understand why it happened like that, Adu. All of us have wept, but we don't understand. God makes the rain, makes the wind, makes trees, creates human beings. We need water to survive. The very things that help us to live can at the same time destroy us. Adu, I too don't understand.'

This time Adu looked as though he understood. It was not what Yaro had said that unlocked his mind but how he said it. If there was one thing that made him like Yaro, it was his sincerity. 'If a man has a son... Now, Adu, if it ever came to the notice of your father that people were planning to kill you, what do you think your father would do?' Adu looked down. He knew his father wouldn't be happy, but he didn't want to talk.

'Would you be happy if somebody killed your own son?' Adu shook his head.

'Would you say the killing of God's Son was a good thing?' Adu was about to shake his head when he remembered that the question of God's Son dying was central to his friend's many talks and he always referred to it as good news. He was silent.

'I want you to tell me, Adu; was it?'

Adu nodded.

'I'm not trying to say, my small friend, that what has happened to you and your father and all of us in this village is good—no. But what I'm saying is that God is able to bring something good out of a bad situation.' Adu nodded.

'There's also one thing that I know...' Yaro said, and then rose up to draw the small curtain covering the window of his room. When he sat down again he continued, '...and that is that God prepares each of us before he allows us to die. How do you think he does this?' Adu remained silent.

'About a week ago I happened to walk with your mother and Yaa on the way from the stream. I had gone to visit my traps and they were returning from the stream.' Adu's raised eyebrows betrayed his interest. 'I always knew that your mother believed the things I've been telling the people of this village. Yaa too believed. That is why I know we shall see them again.'

At that, to Yaro's surprise, Adu broke down and wept. He wept hard and his body shook. Yaro took the grieving boy in his arms and allowed him to cry.

12

Nimo woke up late, feeling tired and sick. Adu lay beside him. It had been raining all night. In all his life in Susa he had never seen a rainy season like this one; a rainy season which had cost him so much. The events of the past two months would take years to clear from his mind.

Nimo felt grateful to the people of the small village for their help and support during the period of mourning. He knew, however, that nobody, nothing, could replace his wife and daughter. He wondered a thousand times how he could live without his wife. His sister Goma had gone back to Buama. Only twice in the past two months had he been to his cocoa farm, just to look around; only once to his rice farm. As he lay in bed that morning he decided that he would go and visit the rice farm. He woke Adu.

'Go and ask Mahama if he can go with us to see the farm this morning.' Normally there was no question about asking Mahama whether or not he wanted to go to farm, but he was sick; he had been sick since the bad news hit the house. Adu returned with the message that Mahama said he was not feeling well.

'Maybe his head aches again,' Nimo said as he got ready to go to the farm. He went to Mahama's room.

'How is it?' Nimo asked Mahama. 'Have you taken some of the medicine?

'Yes. It is becoming better than it was in the night.'

'Take some rest, Mahama. Adu and I will go to the rice farm and be back soon.'

The sun was already rising above the trees when Nimo

and his son made their way towards the swampy area of the land. When they got to the farm they saw that last night's rain had done some damage. Large areas had been swallowed up in the floods. As they stood watching, Adu could hear frogs croaking far and near as if in mockery. The river itself was flooded; but they were at least thankful that the log which they always used to cross the river was intact. Nimo and Adu walked towards the log. Deliberately Nimo struck the flat side of his machete against a tree and shouted at the same time. A great flock of birds flew up over their heads. Some of them simply perched in the trees, ready to return to their booty.

Cautiously Nimo stood on the log-bridge. He was followed by Adu. The river rushed beneath them. Gradually they inched along. They were halfway across when birds feeding on the rice nearby suddenly fluttered up and came diving over their heads. The unexpected movement frightened Adu and he lost his balance. Nimo looked back to see his boy falling into the water. Impulsively he threw his machete away and jumped after him. Nimo got hold of Adu before the boy could submerge. With one hand he grabbed the log and with the other he held his son.

'Hold the log fast,' Nimo shouted. Adu threw his arm round the slippery log and hung on to it while the water rushed past him. Nimo eased himself out onto the log again. Then he held Adu by both hands and pulled him to safety. But as Nimo swung Adu from the water the force of his action threw him off balance. When Adu had wiped his eyes and could see again, his father was not beside him. He glanced below and saw Nimo struggling to get hold of the log. Fear gripped him. In desperation he stretched out his hands to his father. But the man's head was going under for the second time. Adu cried out in alarm. A splash in the water made him turn quickly and then he saw his father surfacing.

Nimo breathed heavily and clung to the log. He spat out a mouthful of water. 'Adu,' he shouted, 'get off the log.' Adu rushed to the bank. Once safe, he looked back to see his father gradually easing himself onto the log once more. He watched in suspense.

Nimo was almost out of the water when the log, rotten from many days of being soaked in the water, snapped. Down went the log and Nimo into the water. Adu's heart beat fast with fright as he waited to see his father surface. Minutes went by. But only the regular rush of the water could be heard. There was no sign of his father.

Crazy with fear Adu sped towards the village, calling and screaming at the top of his voice. He went straight to Appiah's house and collapsed in the compound.

Appiah had heard the screams, and was coming out to see what was happening. He saw Adu fall and was quick to lift him up. But Adu was unconscious. Alarmed, Appiah put him on a mat and called for a man from the village to revive him. Then he rushed to Nimo's house. He met Mahama at the entrance.

'Who was that crying?' Mahama asked.

'Adu. He entered my house wailing and fell down in my compound before anybody could ask him anything. Right now he's fainted. What's the matter? Where is Nimo?'

'Oh no!' Mahama cried. 'Nimo went to visit the rice farm with Adu—not long ago.'

'How come Adu came back alone crying? What went wrong?' Appiah was getting worried.

'Let's go to the rice farm,' Mahama shouted, setting off at a run, followed by a group of village people, drawn by the shouts and screams.

'Look at the log,' Mahama shouted, 'it's broken!' All the people stood silently watching the little river, now bursting with water, and the broken log which was buried in it. No one seemed to know what to do. They were still standing on the bank of the river when they heard someone running towards them. It was the man from the village who had stayed with Adu.

'Nimo,' the panting man announced, 'he's under that log!' At once several men rushed into the deep water. They emerged from the river with the body of Nimo.

No one in Susa, not even the oldest man in the village, could remember a time like this. Here was a family, almost wiped out. People refused to believe that this could happen in their own village. To some it was like a dream, they would soon wake to find it gone. But the reality hung over the village like dark clouds. It was a tragedy, a sorrow, a menacing omen. It could not be true. Such things didn't happen in real life. Maybe they happened in distant lands; but not so close to them. Yet an almost empty house reminded them that Nimo and all but one of his family were no more. So ominous was the situation that people thought of Adu as the last victim waiting to be slaughtered by whatever malevolent hand had caused all this. Then Adu would follow his father, mother and sister into the world of the dead.

To Adu it felt like a dream, a nightmare that scares you until day breaks and vanishes to the back of your mind. He waited for the day to break soon.

Mahama was a walking shadow. He was afraid now for his own survival. Mahama and Adu were living with Appiah and his family. In no time Mahama decided that he would leave Susa before his turn came.

When he told Appiah the older man said, 'Mahama, those who run away from trouble often meet it. You're planning to leave this village because of what has happened to all of us. You should consider that trouble is everywhere. Don't let this trouble drive you away from this place. Stay with me: you will be able to make some money here.'

Mahama listened to him, but he had already made up his mind to go away. He was not alone. The events had made it too scaring for some to remain in Susa. Only a month later, two families left the village with flimsy reasons which did nothing to satisfy inquirers.

Yaro did not know what to say to his friend Adu. Only a few months ago when the first tragedy occurred, he had told

Adu that God was able in the worst of situations to bring out something better. But surely the death of Adu's father could not be the better thing? Was his statement still true? He had no answer. He could only let the boy come to his room and unburden his soul for as long as he wanted, and cry with him and hold the boy in his arms. It was a tragedy to which he had no ready answers. In the silence of his room he prayed that God himself would talk to the boy.

Appiah and his wife were also dazed with the tragedy. The woman was so overcome with grief that the mere sight of Adu made her break down. She offered to keep Adu in her own room at night to provide him with motherly care and comfort. But people told her that would destroy the boy emotionally. Their advice seemed cold but it soon proved necessary.

Nimo's only next of kin, Goma, organized the funeral. Thirty days after Nimo's death, Goma said goodbye to the people of Susa. Many had thought she would wait until after the traditional forty days of mourning, but Goma said she had other priorities in Buama to attend to. She would carry out the forty-day ceremonies there.

'Thank you for your help,' she said, amidst sorrowful sighs from people who had come to bid them farewell. 'It's plain to me that my brother had good friends here. I know his spirit will continue to thank you for many years to come.'

Many wept. The two friends Boye and Adu looked at each other in the compound and embraced one another in a tearful farewell. Mahama and Yaro, men who were said never to cry, shed tears freely. The whole of Susa stood by as Goma, Ama and Adu set off for the train station two miles away, led and followed by some who intended to see them off.

Adu turned round for a last glimpse of the village where he had been born and bred and the people he was leaving behind. He whispered a silent goodbye.

PART TWO

13

When the train arrived at the station Adu quickly detached himself from all the people who had come to bid him goodbye and took his seat. He sat alone by a window. He fixed his gaze on the countryside as far as his eyes could see. Would he ever see those places again? He tried to concentrate on something, but nothing seemed to hold together in his mind.

All these things were like a dream to him. Barely three months ago he had been a happy boy, with the world at his feet, and parents and a sister he loved and who loved him. Now his life had suddenly become small, as if squeezed into a bottle.

He knew no other father but Nimo; no other mother but Birago; no other sister but Yaa. Now he had to spend the rest of his life with no father, a mother he dreaded, a sister who was a stranger to him and a town he wasn't familiar with.

Who was this woman? He feared Goma and would rather have gone somewhere else, but he had no choice.

He was not aware of the train pulling out of the station. When he came to himself they were deep into the journey. Trees and shrubs close to the rails whisked past. He detached himself from the inside world and glanced quickly at Goma and her daughter. The silence was depressing. Why hadn't they said a word to him all through the journey? He looked at Ama, the girl he could not quite connect with her mother. She looked different physically and her friendliness was unmistakable. When Adu looked their way, Ama moved from beside her mother and joined him, as if she were

waiting for that. 'It's a beautiful place out there,' Ama said, pointing at the passing scenery of cultivated farms. Adu just nodded. He knew the girl was trying to draw him out but he wasn't sure he wanted that. 'Have you been to this area before, Adu?' Adu shook his head but kept quiet. 'Our school in Buama is a very interesting place,' Ama tried again. It was a statement but it seemed to demand his response. He recognized the girl's attempts and gave up his resistance.

'Which class are you?' Adu asked. Then remembering that Ama had told him some time ago, he added, 'I've forgotten what you told me the other time.'

'Class five,' Ama said, 'and our teacher is a Miss—the only Miss in the school.'

'What's her name?'

'Miss Beckie Annan.'

Ama waited for Adu to initiate more dialogue, but when it wasn't forthcoming she said, 'You'll be in class six. The class six teacher's name is Mr Ofori. We call him Teacher Ofori. He too is a nice man.' Adu nodded and kept quiet.

Ama left him to his thoughts, and he realized then how much she had done to change his cold attitude. Ama had given him something to look forward to, at least: school life in the town and the interesting teachers.

Goma had so many goods with her that she hired some boys at the Buama train station to help carry the items to the house. As they passed by all the houses, Adu tried to look around the town. The first thing that struck him was its neatness. The whitewashed buildings lined the main road that seemed to divide the town in two. Joined to this main road were tiny streets that led into the suburbs. There were many old buildings. An old town, Adu observed. He saw people looking at them; others were waving at Ama who waved back.

In an open space on his left he saw the chief's palace. He could tell it was a palace by the decorations and shrines in the compound. Someone was beating on the talking drums, the

90

drums that carried messages to the people. He saw the market square; some people in the market stopped and gaped at them.

Soon they got home. Adu took time to survey the family home that he had once overheard his father and aunt rowing over. Part of it had fallen, and been converted to a large chicken coop. The sight of fowls playing about in the small compound gave him warm feelings, reminding him of Susa.

There were three big rooms in the house and a small one. He was told that the small room was his. In Susa he used to share the same room with his mother and sister. Ama lived with her mother in one room.

That night, before he went to bed, his aunt paid him a surprise visit. She told him what his duties were in the house. She didn't like lazy people, she told Adu. She talked about him joining Ama at school that week. When she left, Adu was sure he didn't like her. Still there seemed to be a wall between them. He feared her.

The first six months in Buama passed by slowly and sadly for Adu. He found himself part of the town; he found a place in the home of his aunt's family. He became an accepted pupil at the Buama Primary School. And he found himself a friend.

One of the people who had come to see them on Adu's first day of arrival was a woman who very much reminded him of one of the women back in Susa. She was short and dark with two tribal marks on both cheeks. The gap in the middle of her upper teeth made her look cheerful when she talked. Everybody in the community called her Anane's mother. Her son, who was three years older than Adu, was the class prefect in Adu's class. His mother's real name was Mansa. This woman had a secret in her heart that she would reveal one day.

Adu and Anane became friends a few days after he arrived. Anane took him out one evening to show him interesting places in the town. Anane stammered slightly, which made

91

him a slow talker, but he was very intelligent. He was the top boy in class in all the exams; that was what won him the position of class prefect. Their teacher, Ofori, whom Adu had also begun to like, often referred to Anane as an example of an obedient and clever boy.

One afternoon Anane showed him round town and they ended up at the chief's compound, where a traditional dance was in progress.

'Do they dance l-l-like that in Susa?' Anane stammered.

'No. I've never seen this before.'

'You'll see a lot of it here al-almost every Sa-Sa-turday,' Anane said. One good thing about this boy Adu was grateful for: if he said he had never seen or heard anything, or if he said he didn't know anything, Anane did not laugh at him. The other boys in school did, especially the less intelligent ones, he observed.

When they returned home that evening Goma was waiting. 'Look here, Adu,' she said, 'you simply don't belong to yourself in this place, you hear? Where were you?'

'Aunt, we were watching the dance at the chief's palace.'

'You should never go anywhere without letting me know. You're a stranger here and I don't like any fool in Buama to come and insult me because of you.'

Adu retired to bed that evening feeling confused. It was not what his aunt had said that bothered him but the way she had said it. For some time now his aunt had seemed to pick on him for the slightest thing he did, things he often did back in Susa without any problem.

As he lay in his bed he remembered one incident that had really shocked him. Only last week he had returned from school looking dirty because of playing games at school. He went over to greet his aunt who was peeling some cocoyams, but before the greetings were out of his mouth his aunt shouted, 'Hey Adu! What is this?' Adu looked down at his uniform.

'We played games at school today, Aunt,' he had explained. But he was not quite prepared for what followed: 'You played your father and your mother! Where do you think I get soap for you to wash your clothes? Pluck it from trees? Right, then. This weekend ask me for soap.' She resumed the peeling of the cocoyams. Adu had remained standing, partly out of surprise and partly because it would be disrespectful if he went away before he was asked to.

'Get out of here!' his aunt had shouted without looking up. Surprised and miserable he had gone to his room to think it all over.

Some of the things he used to fear about this woman were beginning to be real. She had a strong in-built hatred of him, a hatred that was linked to his father. He could still hear them arguing over something back in Susa. He never got to know what the rift was all about, but he knew he had become the ultimate victim of the strained relationship that had existed between his father and his aunt. He slept that night a troubled boy.

14

The heat of the day scorched Adu as he trotted towards the school block. Ama ran after him. As they drew close to the hedge at the entrance of the school, Adu slowed down. The school was a hundred yards away. Apart from a few boys and girls tiptoeing by the doors to their classrooms, the compound was empty. Ama took advantage of the slow pace and caught up with Adu. Although younger, she was as tall as her cousin. Only she was plumper, and her breasts were growing heavy. Her school uniform fitted perfectly. Her fair skin stood out in contrast to her dark-blue uniform with the white collar.

'We're late, Ama,' Adu reported, 'and we are in trouble.' Buama Primary School had a highly disciplined headteacher who insisted on punctuality and had inculcated this into all the teachers. Adu and Ama ran towards the school. A girl was once commended during assembly for running at full speed when she was five minutes late. 'That is a sign,' the headteacher had said, 'that in spite of being late she still did her best to maintain punctuality. Unlike some of you, especially the girls who walk majestically to school when you know very well that you're late.' Since that day many pupils could be seen running to school, more so if a teacher was in sight.

That afternoon no teacher was in sight; they were busy with their classes. Ama whispered a goodbye to Adu and dashed towards the primary five classroom. Adu was surprised to find some commotion in his own classroom. The teacher was not there.

'Wow, how lucky I am,' he said as he walked to his desk and sat down, unbuttoning his khaki shirt to allow in some fresh air. Then he looked up. Some of the pupils were standing by the blackboard writing. Anane was among them. He pretended that he didn't see his friend Adu. One of the boys who saw Adu arriving and noticed that the prefect was not doing anything about it was Charlie, the bully. He went to Anane the prefect and whispered something into his ear. Anane nodded and remained standing. A few seconds later the boy went back to him and whispered. Anane looked at Charlie angrily and blurted out in his usual stammer, 'I-I-I know. I've s-seen him.'

'Then write his name, if you've seen him.'

'Mind y-your own business, Cha-Cha-Charlie, and leave mine t-t-to me.' Then, as if he just remembered an appropriate quote, he added, 'P-P-Paddle your own ca-ca-canoe.' As the class prefect, Anane tried hard to keep the other boys in order so that they would respect his position. But while some of the boys readily did as he said there were others—like Charlie—who interfered with his job. Anane knew that he had won the position of class prefect with his intellect and not his physique. Physically most of the boys were bigger than him. Some of the bigger boys vied jealously for the position he held, and he knew this.

Charlie remained standing, towering over the prefect. Anane read the message in the big boy's eyes and didn't like it.

'I-I-know,' he told Charlie. 'I'll write h-h-is na-na-name.' His voice this time was calmer.

'I know he's your friend,' Charlie said, pointing a threatening finger at the prefect. 'He's late, and you must write his name.' His finger was still pointing at Anane when, apparently angered by the overbearing bully, Anane shouted, 'I say, I'll write his name! So mind your own business.' When Anane was angry he scarcely stammered at all.

Alerted by Anane's voice, Adu looked up. He was in time

to see Charlie withdrawing his threatening finger.

'What's going on?' Adu asked. He rose to his feet, and was just about to go forward when the teacher entered. Quickly he sat down again. Someone sounded the familiar cat-call 'Tsh...tsh...tsh' and like a flash everyone darted to his seat almost by instinct. In seconds the noisy class had become as silent as a graveyard.

Ofori, the class teacher, took his seat without a word. He was returning from the headteacher's office. He removed the register from his drawer and opened it. Every eye was on him.

Teacher Ofori was short and stout. Short people, it was said, were impatient and intolerant, but he rarely lost his temper. He stroked his smooth chin as he leafed through the attendance register. For five minutes silence reigned in the class. It was like eternity to the boys. One peculiar characteristic of their teacher was his ability to hold them in disturbing suspense.

Adu gazed at the teacher. In many ways Ofori surprised him. His white shirt sparkled against the blazing sunshine outside. Adu admired the man, especially for his ability to command the respect of the class without the use of force. Ever since his transfer from Susa to Buama Adu had secretly adored Teacher Ofori.

Ofori stood up, and the class came to life. He took the cane from the table, dropped it, and picked a chalk instead. Then his eyes caught the writing on the board. He read it twice, smiled, and looked at the class. Some of the girls were giggling.

'Clean the board,' Ofori instructed. Charlie went forward and took the duster. It was a job he liked doing.

'Anane,' the teacher called, taking his seat again, 'bring the list.' Anane took up the piece of paper containing a list of all the latecomers. He gave it to the teacher. 'I can see here,' Ofori said, 'that these are all habitual latecomers.' The class was silent. 'Come forward if you hear your name.' Ofori took the cane and began to call the names.

'Charlie!'

'Sir.' He went forward.

'Ababio!'

'Sir.' He went forward.

There were eleven names in all, eight boys and three girls. Adu's name was not mentioned. He bent his head guiltily. He knew his friend Anane had favoured him, and he knew that some of his mates were unhappy about it. Charlie eyed the prefect with annoyance. Anane refused to look in his direction and so he didn't see the familiar gestures that the boy made. Adu did not like the way the latecomers were looking at him. He decided that he would give himself up. But that, he reasoned, would betray his friend, make him angry, and thereby destroy the cordial relationship that existed between them. He changed his mind.

Teacher Ofori looked at the eleven pupils in front. He was a strict disciplinarian, but quite often he tempered justice with mercy, sparing culprits the punishment due to them. Yet he thought that eleven pupils late in one afternoon was not a thing to be taken lightly.

'You never learn a thing,' he addressed the whole class. 'Suppose an inspector came in this afternoon on roll check, what would I tell him about why so many of you were late? And did you know,' he asked them as he often did, 'that people lose their well-paid jobs in offices and factories just for reporting late to work?' He paused to allow the words to sink into the children. He gazed at the latecomers, and the sparkle in his eyes told the rest of the story. 'The man is serious,' one girl whispered to another.

'Take the cane,' he told the nearest boy to him. The boy hesitated.

'Take it.'

The boy took it, trembling.

'Now give any of the boys in front four whips on their bottom.'

The seated class began to laugh into their palms when they realized what was going to happen. The boy holding the cane

97

looked unhappily at his mates and remained standing.

'Do it!' commanded the teacher. The boy went to the smallest among them. The small boy didn't resist. Instead he looked angrily at his assailant. He received his four strokes calmly.

'Now take the cane, Ababio,' the teacher told the small boy, 'whip him in return.'

After the punishment Teacher Ofori looked at the class and wondered whether they understood the role of discipline in moulding their characters. Experience, he thought, would be their best teacher.

15

Adu was sick. The drumming in his head threatened to split his brains. The drum was close to his eyes; the eyes themselves refused to close. Every time he attempted to close them they burned as though pepper were stuffed behind the retina. Yet when they were open for too long they threatened to pop out of their sockets. It was already daybreak and he knew his aunt would soon call him. He placed the back of his palm on his forehead. It was warm. Adu moaned softly. He tried to sit up on his mattress, but he could see the room turning round. He began to shiver.

Then he heard the squeaking of a door, followed by footsteps. The violent rapping on his own door echoed through his head.

'Adu, Adu, Adu!' Silence. He knew it was his aunt. He felt all the more sick. 'Auntie!' he responded feebly.

'Fie! Fie! Can't you see it is daybreak? Do you want me to go to the stream and bring you water? If you don't get up right now you'll see what will happen to you.'

Adu heard the footsteps going back the same way they came. He tried to get up, but everything went dark and he fell sprawling on the edge of the mattress. Unable to regain his balance he fell on the bare cement floor. The effect of the fall numbed his head.

He could hear people rushing past his window. They were going to the stream. He must try to join them if he wanted to escape the wrath of his aunt.

He made another attempt to get up. Holding on to the wall for support he stood still for some time. The dancing wall

99

began to steady. He was about to hold on to the handle of the door and turn the knob when he heard footsteps across the yard, this time they approached fast. He hung onto the wall and waited for the worst.

The force of Goma's weight against the door threw it open, hurling the woman into the room.

'Stupid beast,' she yelled at Adu, striking his head with a fist. 'You're still standing here! Who do you think should go to the stream? Who? Get out of here and let me have peace of mind. A fool like you!' She paused for breath. 'And you must fill the tank before you can leave this house today.' She stormed out of the room.

Adu struggled to steady himself. The thud in his head seemed to give way to a lump in his heart. When the lump broke, it did not spill tears from his eyes. Instead it revealed his old hatred for his aunt, the woman who had become a thorn in his flesh. His heart seethed with an enormous grudge. He hated her so deeply he felt he could kill her.

He walked slowly towards the large bucket at the edge of the square compound.

Goma heard a knock at her door and came out to see who was there.

'Good morning, Ma-ma-madam,' Anane greeted her, bowing in a rehearsed respect. Goma nodded her response. 'Is-is-is Adu in, Ma-ma-madam?'

'Adu is not in. He's not back from the stream yet. He slept until the sun was up before he even got up. That lazy boy. You can go and leave him.' Goma hated her own response. Why should she tell a lie to a schoolboy? Did she not have the power to say what she wanted? She was about to go back into her room when Anane asked, 'How about Ama?'

'Ama!' Goma called her daughter. Ama responded from the room. 'Ama, come out and go with Anane. You'll be late.'

Ama forced her way past her mother's side, as she stood obstructing the doorway. Goma shifted. Ama came out with a comb in her hands and her dark long hair still half-combed.

As soon as he saw Ama, Anane asked, 'A-a-a-Ama, where's Adu?' No sooner had the words left his mouth than he regretted having spoken them. Goma, who was on her way back into her room, came out. The look on her face scared Anane.

'What do you mean by that question?' she addressed Anane who stood gaping at her. 'Didn't I tell you where Adu was?'

'Y-you did, Ma-madam.'

'Then why do you ask Ama? Do you suppose I was telling you a lie?'

'Not that, Ma-madam,' Anane attempted an explanation.

'Then why did you ask Ama? Go away. Go. I don't want any explanations. Disrespectful boy. I don't know what they teach you in that school of yours these days. A small boy like you, implying that an older person is lying. Go away with your troubles. I respect your mother. Go away.' Goma vanished into her room. Anane made a face at Ama and began to walk away. At the entrance he met Adu returning from the stream. His shirt, torn in three places, was drenched. Water splashed from the full bucket and ran over his hair down into his eyes and into his mouth. He wiped his face with his palm and forced a smile upon seeing his friend.

'Take the lead, Anane, I'll be following soon,' Adu said and entered the house.

Ofori called the last name in the register. Without waiting to hear the response he ticked present. He had seen the girl in class that morning when he came in. But the response delayed. He looked up.

'Present!' The girl pushed back a stray hair and looked away apologetically.

Ofori looked through the twenty-five names in the register and saw that every pupil was present—except one. He placed a cross by the name of the absentee.

'Where's Adu?' he asked calmly. Every eye turned to

Adu's seat but nobody spoke. 'Anane, where's Adu?' Anane recalled Adu just as he had left him. He wondered whether he should tell the teacher all this. 'I-I-I don't know, s-s-sir.' The impact of the lie spread across the prefect's face, and he blinked continuously.

'You don't know?'

'No, sir,' and the eyes blinked faster and faster.

'Go and call Ama.'

Anane went to the primary five classroom. Beckie Annan, the teacher, stopped talking and waited for him to walk forward. Anane stood at ease, saluted the teacher, and whispered something to her. Beckie looked in Ama's direction. Some of the class followed her gaze.

'Ama!'

'Yes, madam.' The girl rose to her feet.

'Follow him.'

Anane whispered, 'Thank you, madam.' He saluted lightly and went out.

'Where are we going?' Ama asked.

'Just follow me.'

'Who wants me?' Ama asked again.

'Just follow me.'

When they got to the primary six classroom, Adu had arrived and was standing in front of the teacher. His head was bowed, his face was tearful.

'Ama,' Ofori called.

'Sir.'

'Tell us why Adu is late. I asked him and all he can do is cry. Tell us why he's late.' Ama looked at Adu, then at the class, who stared at her. 'I don't know.'

'You don't know?'

Ama shook her head.

'Were you late too?'

'No, sir,' she replied and waited for the next question. But Ofori allowed silence to speak for him. He knew that Adu was in a difficult situation. Ofori cast his mind back a few weeks. He remembered the scene vividly. Ofori had had a long chat with the headteacher that windy evening. It looked as if their talk was likely to eat into the night. So he had called Adu and told him to carry his books home for him. Ofori recollected the enthusiasm with which the boy had obeyed him. It was every schoolboy's privilege and joy to be sent to a teacher's house. But he had had the surprise of his life when he returned from the headteacher's office that night to find Goma waiting for him at the door.

'Mr Ofori,' he could still hear the sarcasm in Goma's voice, 'I beg you, is it true that you sent Adu?'

'Oh yes, madam,' Ofori had replied most politely. 'I asked him to bring my books home on his way to school. Is he all right, madam? I hope he's not gone about some mischief.'

'Well, he has...'

'Oh no, what did he...'

'Let me finish,' Goma had cut in, 'let me finish. That boy is naughty, very naughty. He seizes every opportunity to run away from his duties at home, so I don't like people sending him without my knowledge.'

Shocked. Yes, he had been shocked. In all the ten years he had been teaching, never had he encountered a parent of Goma's type. No parent ever questioned him on such a trivial matter as sending a pupil home with books, something the boys themselves enjoyed doing. That day he had suppressed his anger. The following day he had asked Adu, 'Where did you go yesterday after you took my books home?'

'I went home, sir.'

'Did you pass anywhere before reaching home?'

'No, sir. I went home straight.'

He had worn the same innocent face that morning as he did now. Ofori had later found out more about Goma and his sympathy for Adu had grown.

Yet Ofori knew that one pupil could not be given special treatment. Adu should face the same treatment that the other pupils received. He knew that Adu could be hardened against authority because of what he suffered at home. He could even destroy himself with bitterness and holding a grudge.

'All right, Ama,' Ofori said. 'Thank you; you may go.' Ama thanked the teacher, glanced quickly at Adu, and walked back to her classroom.

'For being late, you'll receive your punishment. Follow me.' Adu and the teacher went out. Anane followed them wide-eyed. From the direction they went he knew Adu was going to be given a portion of the school garden to weed.

'You see that cassava tree over there?' Ofori asked when they reached the school garden. Adu nodded. 'Clear the weeds from this pole to the stump over there—down to the cassava. You will do this during the lunch break.'

'Yes, sir.'

Then, in a friendly tone, Teacher Ofori asked, 'Why were you late, Adu?'

'I went to the stream five times today because my aunt told me that unless the big drum was filled I couldn't come to school.'

Ofori nodded. 'Was it a punishment?' he asked.

'I don't know, sir. I had a headache during the night, so I waited a bit before I could get up from bed.'

Ofori looked at the boy standing before him. Adu's eyes were protruding and his khaki shorts had sunk to below his waist. His arms were thin and his hands looked frail beneath the short sleeves of his white shirt. In a situation like this Ofori would rather have chosen the spirit of the law than the letter. But he was convinced that Adu needed genuine discipline to counteract the false one he seemed to be receiving from his aunt. He decided to keep an eye on the boy.

He turned to go, but remembered something else. 'Don't punish those pupils by making them work in the school garden,' the headteacher had said at a staff meeting one day. 'If you do, you teach them to hate farming—and the worst harm you can do a person is to make him hate to work in the farm.'

'Listen, Adu,' Ofori said. 'Remember that this is not a punishment. Do it not as a punishment but as a lesson. Gardening is part of the school curriculum. Do you understand?'

'Yes, sir.'

As soon as the bell for closing rang, shouts of jubilation sounded in all the classes. It signalled the close of the day; time to go home. For the majority of the pupils this bell was the hammer that broke their chains for the day. Until the next day, they were free from classwork, difficult mathematics, spelling drills, and above all the canes of tough teachers.

That it was Friday increased the excitement. Until they returned to the prison of the classroom on Monday there lay ahead of them two solid days when they were the masters of their own lives—except for their parents, but they were not as difficult to handle as the teachers. Some of them danced for joy. Here and there a boy hit a girl and dashed away, or risked being beaten by jumping over the flowering hedges, which the teacher had forbidden. Adu and Anane strolled out of the classroom hand in hand and joined the rest at the parade grounds.

The teachers came out and stood in front. The headteacher was the last to come.

'Attention!' he commanded. Every pupil stood erect. The headteacher, standing at attention himself, scanned the pupils as if to ascertain that everybody was present. As he turned from left to right, the setting sun fell on his bald head and flashed like glass. Some of the girls saw it and suppressed their giggles. They called him Motorway because of his bald head.

Motorway sniffed loudly and shouted, 'Stand at ease!' The pupils stood with legs apart and stared at him, expecting the next command.

'Attention!' They obeyed.

'At ease! Attention! At ease! Now the day is over...'

105

The voices rang out in chorus, some too high, others too low, in their usual discordant croaking. But they sang with vigour: *Now the day is over; Night is drawing nigh; Shadows of the evening; Steal across the sky.*

What followed next was the usual routine: 'The national anthem...the Lord's prayer...Eyes open.' A boy could close his ears and go through the traditional sequence without missing anything out.

'Any announcements?' Motorway asked, turning to the teachers behind him. Most of them shook their heads. He heard footsteps from the girls' section and turned to look. It was the girls' prefect. Motorway sniffed noisily, pushed his glasses up his oversized nose and gazed at Mary as she came along. Her starched and neatly-pressed blue uniform flapped on her thighs as she went forward. Dark in complexion, she stood a few inches taller than the headteacher. All eyes turned to her as she approached Motorway, a piece of paper in her hand. Motorway stretched out his hands to take the paper, but Mary stopped for a moment, a bit nervous. 'It's for Miss Annan,' the prefect said.

'Okay—for you, Beckie,' Motorway shouted to the only female on his staff. Beckie Annan came a few steps forward and took the piece of paper from the girl. While she read, Mary leaned towards her and whispered something into her ear.

'It's the PE thing,' Beckie told the headteacher, who was waiting to hear what it was about. 'The results of the performance tests of the week—from the girls' side.'

'Oh yes,' Motorway said, pushing up his glasses and standing aside for Beckie to address the school.

During the week marks were awarded to or deducted from every section for good performance or wrongdoing by pupils in that section. The marks were for neatness, punctuality, brilliance in class, creativity and sports. Every Friday these marks were compiled and the results announced.

'Now listen to the results of this week's performances,'

106

Beckie said in her usual calm voice. At twenty-four Beckie knew her small world well. She taught with confidence and was conscientious, which was why the headteacher liked her. Attractive Beckie Annan made heads turn whenever she passed by.

When Beckie had finished announcing the results, Motorway took over. 'Attention,' he shouted. The pupils obeyed.

'Left turn.'

There was a little pandemonium. Some of the pupils turned right instead, saw their colleagues facing left and tried to correct their mistake.

'Right turn!' This time almost everyone got it right.

'About turn!' A commotion followed. 'Right turn...left turn...about turn...' The confusion ran high as everyone turned wherever he pleased. Even after Motorway had stopped issuing commands they kept turning.

'You're dismissed,' the final command came. The whole school broke into joyful hurrays! and rushed helter-skelter. Their freedom until Monday was eventually secured. Adu saw Ama and Anane rejoicing with the others as they rushed towards home. He watched them go. Then he went round the school block. He picked up a machete from under the hibiscus flowers and headed towards the school garden.

Beckie Annan packed her books, as if ready to go home, but she lingered awhile. A few of the girls were still arranging their things in the class. She waited. When they left, Beckie sat down, rested her head on the table and allowed her mind to wander.

Ofori. Yes, that was the man who occupied her mind. Until a year ago she hadn't thought there was her type of man in the school. But now she couldn't take her eyes off Ofori: so strong willed, intelligent, lovely. But since when? Ofori hadn't struck her as attractive until very lately. *Beckie! What has happened to you?* No one dared approach Beckie more than once with anything to do with love. Some of the

107

teachers had given up making advances towards her; she knew how to discourage them. Like Afram, the class three teacher. From the way the man used to gaze at her she knew that he too had been captivated. But unlike most of the others, Afram dared to visit her in her house. As soon as she saw him she knew how to deal with him. She prepared him a lunch. Then, as they sat down to talk, she pulled her album from under the table and went through it with him.

'And who's this?' Afram asked.

'Oh, that is my brother...my father...another brother...a former mate of mine from the secondary school...'

Afram looked at her.

'Oh, well,' she said, 'to tell you the truth, he's my fiancé.' That settled Afram for good.

Men were funny. Beckie smiled.

But perhaps she wasn't so clever after all: for without warning, without struggling, calmly, Ofori had entered her heart. He had captured her mind and heart. A tutor at college used to say, 'Love is not a thing of the mind but of the heart. Your heart can dictate and your mind will obey.' Beckie never believed that. To her, love was a thing of both the mind and the heart. She used to argue that if her mind said No to love, then her heart had no choice but to say No, too. Her opinion had not changed, she told herself firmly. In this situation both mind and heart said Yes. Did this make any sense?

'It makes sense,' she murmured aloud. That was when she realized someone was standing by the door.

'What makes sense?' Ofori asked, stepping into the room and leaning against the teacher's table where Beckie sat.

For a whole minute the young teacher feasted his eyes on hers and she refused to blink. They took their fill of one another—neither satisfied—until Beckie's eyes began to water. They filled and overflowed. Still she refused to blink.

At last Ofori blinked a couple of times. He marvelled at the strength he saw in those eyes.

'Beckie,' Ofori said.

She stood up, 'Let's go,' she said. Ofori took her hands.

They walked silently. At the end of the block Ofori heard somebody weeding and turned to look. It was Adu.

'Look!'

Beckie turned. 'What is it?' she asked.

'Wait for me.' Ofori went towards the boy.

'Adu.'

Adu turned round sharply and then froze. The last person he would have expected. He wiped sweat from his brow and said apologetically, 'I...I was trying to finish this before going home.'

Ofori shook his head disapprovingly. 'No, Adu. I didn't ask you to do this now. You must go home.'

'Yes, sir.' He hid the machete among some young banana trees at the edge of the school garden and began his walk home. Ofori waited until Adu passed him and then followed. 'You know what your aunt is like, Adu,' the teacher said. 'You should not do things that will make her flare up.'

'Yes, sir.'

Adu did not really care. His aunt found fault with him anyway, whether he did the right thing or not. Defying her was no longer anything to be afraid of. He would rather weed the garden and be in his teacher's good books than make any more effort to please his aunt.

Beckie watched the boy as he passed by. He was barefooted and he held on to his khaki shorts to prevent them from sliding down his thin legs. A sudden sadness moved her as she looked at the boy's gloomy face. Adu hurried away and was soon far ahead of the two teachers.

'I've seen this boy a couple of times looking like that,' Beckie said. 'Something about him makes me want to cry.'

'He's a child of grief.'

'A child of grief?'

'Yes. He's in my class. A brilliant boy, I tell you. But he's had more than his share of pain in this world.'

'Why? What's the matter with him?'

'A long story, my dear. I'll tell you some time.'

A brief silence closed the chapter on Adu.

'You wanted to see me,' Beckie said, almost casually.

'Yes,' he replied, 'and I have. Always good to see you.'

Beckie surveyed the man's face and tried to hide a smile, but her dimples had already given her away.

'So you just wanted to see me...just look at me? Haven't you seen enough of me yet?'

'Enough of you! Oh, well, of course I have.' Ofori could not match her sense of fun and he knew it. As they walked by the hedge he plucked a leaf. Unconsciously he placed it on his lips and bit it into shreds. He kicked a stone and reached out to pluck another leaf. Beckie was surprised. She had never seen Ofori so nervous. Plainly he had something to tell her. Maybe she should help him out.

'Tell me,' she said.

'What?'

'What you're hiding.'

'Oh, am I hiding something?'

One look at him, and Beckie knew she couldn't help him out after all.

16

Evening descended upon Buama without warning. It was silent and uneventful. Smoke curling from houses up into the darkening dusk indicated that the women were busy with the preparation of the last meal of the day. Goma and her household were busy with the evening chores. Ama and her mother were peeling plantain for the evening *fufu*.

Suddenly, *Kong-kong, kong-kong, kong-kong!* The sound of the drum broke the quiet evening. The voice of the chief's crier could be heard by people four houses away. They could sit in their houses and listen to whatever announcement the chief had for the people, but they usually preferred to come out. It was a sign of respect for the chief to come out and listen.

'Good evening, sons and daughters of Buama,' the crier began. 'The chief would like all Buama to note: something terrible has happened in our land. The chief and his elders have discovered that some worthless citizens of this town have defiled our land. They have shown disrespect for our chiefs. Two days ago thieves broke into the chief's graveyard and stole gold ornaments and other precious valuables. The chief and his elders are asking the citizens of this town to watch out for the thieves. Anyone who helps the chief to discover the items and catch the thieves will be rewarded.' *Kong, kong, kong!*

The crier made his way to other parts of the town while the people went back to their houses. That was news! To steal from the graveyard was unheard of.

Ama reported the message to her mother, who had refused

to come out as she always did. At first she expressed her dismay at the grave theft. But later she remarked, 'Some traditions must just die out. How can they still be burying gold with the dead chiefs when people go about poor and hungry?'

It was communal labour day. The men of Buama believed in pooling resources to work on community projects. During the week the town council had announced that the school project was due to resume on Friday. They had stopped work at the peak of the farming season, but now that work on the farms had grown less, it was time to complete the renovation of the primary one classroom block. The men asked the headteacher if they could work on a Friday instead of the usual Saturday because there were funerals in the town almost every Saturday. Motorway granted their request, but refused to allow a full holiday for the pupils. Instead he gave them a 'no-class' holiday: the pupils would do some work in the school garden, the games field, or other odd jobs assigned by the teacher on duty.

Anane and Adu strolled hand in hand on the school field. When they reached the classroom where the men were working, an elder who was a friend of Anane's father saw them and called, 'Hey, Anane, look at you, come and carry this rubbish away. And you, Adu. See how your friends are working hard.' He turned to one of the men and said, 'Look at the boy. He's grown like a mushroom. He's already a big boy.'

'When they give birth to you upon a hill,' the other responded with a laugh, 'you grow fast. His father has something on his hands.'

Suddenly Anane felt a sharp paralysing jab in his left foot. He screamed and jumped up. He threw away the board he had been pulling, held on to his foot and began to jump up and down, wailing.

'What is the matter?' shouted the elder who had invited them to work. He rushed to the boy's aid. By this time Anane was rolling on the ground with pain. Someone shouted nearby, 'Snake, snake. Look at it!' Some of the elders attacked the small dark snake. It wriggled under the heavy stones and sticks that were hurled at it but it still made an attempt to escape. While the snake was being battered to death, Anane was moaning in pain. An elder held the wailing boy under his arms and was trying to raise him up when a teacher arrived on the scene. It was Beckie.

'What happened?' she asked.

'He has been bitten by that snake,' replied the elder.

Calmly, Beckie bent down and surveyed the blood oozing out of the boy's left foot.

'Bring him here,' she requested, and turned to go into a classroom. Two elders held the boy and followed her.

Adu had been watching. When they took Anane away, he quietly detached himself from the crowd and dashed into the school garden. When he returned he was holding a bunch of leaves which he had gathered from the thicket behind the garden. There was already a crowd standing around the helpless boy. His mother Mansa was one of them. Someone had already called her. Adu gave the herbs to the woman. 'Please boil this, Anane's mother,' he said. He had hardly finished when someone took the leaves from his hands and dashed off with them into the nearest house. It was Mary, the school's girls' prefect.

Adu knelt down beside his friend. He was holding a brand new razor blade which he borrowed from the school storeroom. He remembered clearly how his father used to handle such cases. He held Anane's injured foot and carefully cut the spot where the snake had bitten. Then he pressed it. Blood oozed out. His father had once told him that such an action was bound to reduce the poison content in the blood.

Next, he ground some of the leaves he had brought from the bush and pasted the residue on the wound. The juice from those leaves could reduce the effect of the poison.

The elders looked on with wonder at the boy's calm and

confident treatment. When Mary brought the boiled leaves Adu poured the concoction into a calabash and allowed it to cool off. Then he forced his friend to swallow the mixture. The reaction was fast. Anane began to cough until he threw up a greenish substance. He continued to cough and throw up. When the coughing abated he looked up and stared at the people around. His eyes met those of his friend and Adu smiled slightly.

'Take him home,' Adu said to Mansa, who was too overcome with shock and relief to say anything.

Adu was thinking about the events of the week that had just passed by. It was evening and he was in his room. He looked at his clothes hanging on the nails behind the door. Two years ago he would have been using those worn old clothes for the farm and other non-school activities but now they were his only school uniform. The patches on the seat of his trousers and on his shoulders were sewn a week ago, after his aunt had complained about his carelessness with clothes. Did Adu think that her sewing-machine was meant for mending the clothes of fools like him?

He closed his eyes. He could see Susa clearly. Teacher Ofori had told him many times to try to forget Susa. But it was the most difficult thing to do. Gradually though, he succeeded in tearing his mind away from the village.

A knock on the main gate to the house interrupted him. When the visitor was told to enter he heard the voices of Anane and his mother. 'Good evening, my friend,' his aunt responded to Mansa's greetings. 'They say that when you mention a person's name he is close by. I had just mentioned your name when Ama and I were talking about the price of tomatoes these days.'

'Boo, mention that again, my friend,' Mansa lamented, sitting on the chair that Ama offered her. 'Now tomatoes have no market.'

'It looks as if the whole of Buama is farming tomatoes,' Goma said. Then she laughed at her own remark. This surprised Ama who was bringing another stool for Anane. Whenever these two women met, her mother was a different person. Mansa was the only woman who could make her mother talk so freely and happily.

On his mattress Adu was thinking the same as Ama, but with his own additions: why was it that his aunt scarcely had regard for anybody except Mansa? He was also surprised that two people so different should be so close. Perhaps it was not always true that only birds of the same feathers flocked together. Those of different feathers could flock together too.

As for Anane, he only gazed at Goma in bewilderment. Until very recently he too had not understood why his mother should find so much favour in the eyes of a woman who made enemies of everybody except her daughter. But now he knew. And what he knew scared him. He had overheard it from his mother. Anane looked at Ama keenly and blinked. Goma said, 'Congratulations, my friend. God has given back your son to us.' She was referring to Anane and the snake bite. 'You heard all the bad talk of Buama's witches, didn't you? They wanted to finish your son for you, my friend.'

'Say it again. They scared me, you know. But my boy is looking strong and healthy. As for God, he's not like those people whose names I don't want to mention. He is so kind to us.' They all looked at Anane who bowed. Ama was amused. She tried to see if Anane was shy so that tomorrow she could tease him at school. But she was disappointed. Anane lifted his head and stared keenly at Ama until the girl looked away. She got up and walked towards Adu's room. As the older women were engaged in matters concerning them, Anane got up too and joined his friends.

After they had gone, as if Mansa had been waiting for the chance, she said, 'Anyway I came here with a matter on hand. It's about my boy Anane...in fact, rather it's about your boy Adu. He saved my son. Everybody in Buama is talking about that. Without his medicine my boy would be

115

dead by now. My friend, I don't want to remind you of any pain, but your brother who was in Susa knew good medicine which he has passed on to his son Adu.'

Goma looked at her friend.

Mansa continued, 'The reason we came here this evening is to show our appreciation for what your boy has done for our family. You know my husband has travelled. I really wanted to wait until he returned. But you see, the elders say that when appreciation is delayed it loses its taste. When my husband returns we shall come again.'

'Ah, my friend,' Goma replied. 'The hill and the antelope have no thanks.'

'I know,' Mansa replied, unwrapping something in a piece of cloth she carried. It was money. 'What I'm doing you should not despise because you know the tradition. Take this and buy something for the boy. It is not payment for what he did, because no one can pay for life.'

Goma took the money. 'You mention tradition, my friend,' Goma said, 'and we mustn't undo tradition. It's for the sake of tradition that I'm accepting this...' But before she put the money away, Adu came out of his room. The two women looked up. Goma ignored him and began, 'The tradition of the fathers must be...'

'I have something to say,' Adu said, as he walked towards the women. It was a bold step that he was taking. Adu knew that. He also knew that what he was about to do could result in repercussions he wasn't ready to bear. Yet he had to do it. The tradition of their fathers? Adu very clearly remembered what his father had said about his tradition of administering healing by herbs. 'About two years ago...' he began.

'Don't tell us stories,' Goma interrupted him.

'No, let's hear him,' Mansa said.

'My father taught me how to stop minor bleeding with cassava leaves. A few weeks after he taught me I used it on a friend who cut himself with a razor-blade. The next day this boy bought sweets and gave me some which I ate. When I told my father about how I helped stop the bleeding, I

116

mentioned that the boy was so happy that he bought sweets for me.' Adu paused when Goma coughed slightly. But they all remained silent and so he continued. 'My father was so disgusted about the sweets that he made me do something that I'll never forget. He made me buy sweets the next day and return them to the boy. It was embarrassing to do this in front of my friends at school. They said I was mean and proud. But my father explained to me that the medicines he administered to people were absolutely free and in no circumstance should I ever receive payment of any kind for them.'

The meaning of Adu's story was obvious. Ama and Anane gaped at him. It was the last thing they expected him to do.

'This is not a gift, my son,' Mansa said. 'This is just...'

'I told my father exactly that...'

'Let her finish,' Goma shouted at Adu. 'When an elder is talking, you don't interrupt. You see what I've been telling you, Mansa? You heard the way he spoke—so proud, so disobedient...and when I try to discipline a child like that people think I'm a bad woman.' Adu noticed the anger in her voice.

'I'm sorry,' Adu apologized.

'Let him go on. Go on, Adu,' Mansa said.

'I told my father that the boy was not buying the sweets because of me. We bought sweets all the time, anyway. But father wouldn't hear that, just because the boy, when he was giving me the sweets, mentioned the help I gave him.'

'So what are you saying?' Goma asked. 'Are you wiser than us here?'

Adu didn't say anything.

'Go to your room at once,' Goma shouted.

'Anane's mother,' Adu said as he walked away, 'I wash my hands of any curse that may come by the giving of that gift.' What Adu said sent sparks of fire through Goma. She got up in fury.

Suddenly Adu felt a sharp pain that went the full breadth of his back. 'You stupid orphan, orphan, orphan; foolish

117

boy, son of a goat. You—a fool like you—insulting your elders and cursing us? Fool, fool, fool.' The words and the whips fell together. Anane and his mother were so shocked that for a moment they didn't know what to do.

Adu's body felt as if it were on fire. He tried to escape. He made for the gate but Goma caught him and pulled him back. His shirt tore in two and sent him crashing onto the cement floor. Goma dragged him along.

Mansa, realizing the seriousness of the situation, pounced on Goma and tried to pull her away from the bleeding boy. Goma gave Adu a final slap and pushed him against the wall. Adu fell with a thud to the hard floor. 'Foolish boy,' Goma shouted. 'Say that again and I'll slaughter you.'

'It's all right, Goma,' Mansa said. 'What did you do that for?'

'Can't you see the boy is stubborn?'

Adu attempted to sit up but everything whirled around so fast he was forced back to the floor. He coughed hoarsely until he choked. He spat blood upon the floor. Ama looked confused. What had caused this sudden attack? She looked at her mother and saw her eyes flaming.

Suddenly Adu rose to his feet, looked his aunt in the eye, and blurted out, 'I hate you! I hate you! I hate you with all my heart. God will pay you for your wickedness! I hate you and I could kill you. Kill you. Kill you.' He coughed till he was out of breath and choked again.

'You could kill who?' Goma spat the words out and moved towards Adu who stood defiantly as if ready to effect his threat. 'It's your mother you will kill, not me,' said Goma, and, as if on second thoughts, she decided to leave the boy alone.

Adu limped to his room and sat on his mattress. As he bowed his head, he began to cry, not so much from bodily pain as from loneliness and sorrow.

He felt a hand touch his shoulder. He looked up. Ama was holding a bucket of water and a towel.

'I'm sorry about this, Adu,' Ama tried to console him. 'I

118

don't know what to say. Mother is too wicked and I don't know why.' Adu was quiet. Ama dipped the towel in the lukewarm water and began to wipe out the dirt and bloodstains from his body.

When Anane and his mother had left the house Goma, still angry, burst into Adu's room. 'You are finished, Adu!' she bellowed. 'Finished. You saw the money they brought? It could have bought your school uniform and paid your fees for one year. Do you think I can always find the money to meet all these expenses? That bad habit your father planted in your head will make you suffer in life. You are finished. Your uniform will remain upon your body like threads.'

She stormed out.

That night Adu had a nightmare. His spirit was broken. He felt the little light in him giving way to darkness. As he tossed about in bed he felt like giving up on life—to say goodbye to this world and be gone for ever and ever. He drifted into darkness against his inner will, as if he was being pushed into a deep well full of many faces.

The faces were weird. He saw a pair of eyes staring at him. He thought he was about to recognize the face when the strange eyes blinked. Now the face was no longer a human face; it was the face of a leopard. Cold fear surged into him as he was forced by a power greater than himself to look at the very object that drove fear into him.

The leopard now rose from the deep well and moved towards him. He screamed and turned towards his parents whom he saw standing beside him. As the leopard approached, everyone dispersed. He saw the beast running after his mother and his little sister. He himself held on tightly to his father as they stood there helpless while the leopard tore them to pieces.

His father rushed to rescue them, but he was too late. Now the leopard turned and ran after his father. Before his eyes the animal attacked his father and conquered him. He screamed and took to his heels. He turned to see the devouring beast dashing after him. When he looked ahead he saw his friend Yaro standing by. Quickly he threw himself upon his friend, panting and fainting. He was sure the animal was going to get them both, but to his surprise the beast stopped short, unable to approach them. Something seemed to be shielding him and Yaro against the approaching force of the beast. He saw the animal spitting fire while gazing at them. Then, as he stared into those fearful eyes, the animal changed into a human being. There before him stood his aunt and her eyes were blazing.

Now his aunt smiled. Adu saw her fangs sticking out and her tongue snarling at him. Cold chills seized him. Was that his aunt? The woman now stretched out her hands and beckoned him to herself. When he vehemently refused to go she got hold of him and tried to pull him by force. He was so shaken that he screamed at the top of his voice and tried to free himself from her grip.

Adu was still screaming when he opened his eyes. He was alone in his room. Quickly he rose to his feet and rushed to the door. When he opened it he saw his aunt and Ama standing there. He screamed and slammed the door shut. Goma went away but Ama opened the door and entered.

'What's the matter, Adu?'

'What?'

'You've been screaming at the top of your voice. We thought something was happening to you.'

'Is it already daybreak?'

'Yes,' Ama replied, and asked with curiosity, 'What happened to you? Was it a bad dream?'

It was a bad dream and Adu didn't attempt to hide it from Ama. He told her everything.

Ama was petrified. 'My mother turned into a leopard?'

'That was what I saw.'

17

He meant every word of it when he said he hated his aunt and that he could kill her. Ama had left his room when a number of ideas came to his mind. He glanced over to the corner of his room and saw his machete leaning against the wall. The first idea hatched quickly: take the machete, rush your aunt from behind, and chop off her head. His heart beat faster as he turned the matter over. Blood pounded in his head and his body shook. His will urged him to act. Hatred for his arch-enemy mounted to flashpoint.

But unconsciously he was holding on tightly to his mattress. He was afraid. He saw Yaro clearly in his mind. His friend would have objected to that idea. He gave it up.

Slowly another idea formed in his mind. It came gradually, like a helper, a comfort, the way to end his troubles. The tension that had built in him began to loosen as he thought about this new idea. Oh yes! He sat on his mattress. He could see it clearly now. Wasn't his father at peace? Did his mother know any suffering now? Not at all. And wasn't Yaa at rest? He saw their faces—peaceful and calm. The state of non-existence was so appealing to him that he was surprised he hadn't thought of it before. There would be no wicked aunt to be bothered about, no mates to mock him, no punishment at school, no forced labour at home, no headache to battle with, no worry at all—like his mother and father and sister.

The thought excited him as he sat on the mattress. He looked at his bleeding elbow, felt the cut on his forehead, and the bruises on his legs. They ached, but nothing to worry about now; it would soon be over.

He got up, took a shirt and wore it over his bleeding wounds. The pain drew his attention but he ignored it: it would soon be over. He felt the weight of his swollen lips. He placed a finger on them and looked at the blood stains. He spat on the floor. What did it matter? He would soon be gone.

He stepped out. Ama saw him open the main gate but she did not interrupt him. His aunt saw him, too, but ignored him. If he was going to sit outside, people were sure to see his swollen lips and bruised hands, she reasoned. But what did it matter?

But Adu wasn't going to sit outside: he had a better idea than that.

He thought about the train. Yes, that would do the work fast and thoroughly. Perhaps it would even carry part of him back to Susa—to be buried with his father, mother, and sister.

He took the pathway towards the train station. Several hundred yards from the station he branched off towards the west where the rails led through to Susa. He waited by the rail. Along it he saw hundreds of canary birds pecking at stray grains. Others had made their nests on palm fronds close by. But these no longer interested him. He followed the rails with his eyes far, far away, where they seemed to narrow gradually until they vanished. He waited.

A gentle wind began to blow. After what seemed to be an endless wait, he thought he heard the booming sound of a train approaching from the direction of Susa. The sound came with the wind, but when the wind died down the sound died with it. He began to feel disappointed. The train too had joined the forces that were militating against him. The train was the one which had transported him from Susa to Buama two years ago, to undergo all this. Even the train was his enemy. The old hatred he bore for his aunt began to well up in him.

He knew a place which, unlike the train, would always be there—that place would not disappoint him. The pain in his bruised leg and lips spread, but he ignored it and made for the place where his comfort lay, peaceful and waiting.

He had to cross the town, and he did so without realizing it. He was heading towards the stream. He knew where he was going. The river in Buama was big and deep in places. He had seen it happen to his father. The water was his best friend now. It would soon happen to him and all would be over.

He hurried to the river and went upstream to a place he knew of, where it was deep and wide. Soon he would be part of it.

There it was. Reaching the place he removed his shirt, stood on the bank and peered at his image. His lips were blood-red. He focussed on his aunt and allowed the hatred to well up in him again. He reflected on his life and all the pain he had experienced, the pain that would soon be gone for ever and ever.

He crouched at the very edge of the deep water, ready to jump in. There was no log to help press him down, he thought, remembering his father, but the water here was deep enough to swallow him. Before he jumped he would think about some of the people he knew. They came easily to mind: Ama, Anane, Teacher Ofori, Beckie, Mahama, Yaa, Mother, Father... He stopped there; the rest could wait. But there was someone else he wanted to remember. He feared he wasn't ready to cope with the consequences of remembering that man. No, he wouldn't recall him; that person would spoil his plans. But he couldn't stop his mind roaming right towards that man in Susa. He wanted to avoid him but there he was, in the little village, working on his farm, sitting in his room, reading from his famous book. There he was, striding in front of him to the nearby village. He focussed on him for a while. So picturesque was the scene that he could not tear his mind from it, though he tried hard. Now Yaro was speaking to him.

'...and there's a place we all go to when our work on this earth is finished.' It was in answer to a question Adu had put

123

to him about what happened to the millions of people who were dead. The scene which he had been trying to put out of his mind, now interested him. He heard himself asking the question, 'And who decides when one's work on earth is finished?' His friend Yaro had turned sharply and looked at him. Then, in his usual patient fashion, he had replied quietly, 'God, my friend; God decides.'

A question formed in his mind now which he had not asked his friend then: supposing—the question was imprinted on his brain—supposing one was tired of life and decided that his work on earth was ended—what about that? Couldn't he decide for himself that his work was done?

From where he was squatting beside the stream Adu waited for an answer, but no reply came. Yaro was no longer beside him.

A fish in the deep, dark water splashed after a worm and alerted Adu. The same hatred he had had for his aunt spilled over against his friend Yaro. Yaro had destroyed his plans. For the first time anger burned in his heart against Yaro. It was he who had just told him he could not decide for himself that his work on earth was finished. What was there left for him to do? His father was dead. His mother was dead. He had no relative who cared for him. Wasn't his life finished? Huh, Yaro? What should I do now? Tell me, Yaro!

And the reply came, though he neither expected it nor wanted it: 'God is able to change even the worst situation to something better.' He found himself in Yaro's room, after his mother's death. Those were the very words Yaro had spoken to him when his mother and sister died. It was in the same season that his father was drowned. What did Yaro tell him about that? He had told him that God had spared his life; it was Adu who was being drowned when his father saved him. His father had sacrificed his life for him, Yaro said. And Yaro had then tried to compare his father with the Saviour he often talked about, who sacrificed his life for all people.

'Your father wants you to live,' Yaro had said. 'He wants you to live for him. His life is ended but yours is not.'

124

Had his life benefited anybody? Adu thought. Wasn't his life full of suffering and misery?

As he walked further upstream, away from Yaro, he felt in his mind a trace of compassion for him. Then he knew how much his friend Yaro had influenced him.

That quality of life he admired in Yaro revived in him a sense of his own worth. The brief encounter had revived something he wanted to hold on to. The pain in his body was at present as real as his hatred for his aunt. But he wanted to live.

He made his way towards a tree further upstream, through elephant thistles that lined the bank of the river. He hadn't the slightest desire to go home, though it was now midday. As he made his way through the thicket and reached the tree, frightened birds flew out above him at the sudden appearance of this intruder. Adu settled under the shady tree. He glanced around him. The large dry leaves which had fallen reminded him of certain parts of his father's cocoa farm in Susa. The grass had made a circle round the tree. He stretched his legs and leaned painfully back on the trunk, gazing up into the many branches.

He saw a yellow bird which stretched its neck up and down to look at the visitor. From where he sat he knew that he could drop that cheeky bird with one pull on a catapult, if he had one. But he doubted whether he was ready to kill. Better things than killing occupied his mind. Besides, he had just attempted one killing and failed; what was the guarantee that he could kill that bird? Times had changed. As the sun tilted towards the far west, twilight stole through the trees. A gentle air swept over his tired eyes. Exhausted from the mental, physical and emotional strain, he soon fell asleep.

Fear gripped Adu when he awoke to find himself in pitch darkness. He had slept too long. Quickly he rose up and groped for the way home. But as he did so he saw a beam of light moving up and down along the very way he had come. He heard quiet voices as two men parted the shrubs and walked towards him.

'We must be fast,' a voice said.

'Let's hide it under that tree,' another voice replied. Why did Adu seem to recognize the second voice? But there was no time to think as the voices approached. He stood there shivering. Should he run?

In a split second he decided to climb the tree. Forgetting the possibility of snakes hanging from or creeping along the tree he climbed up. He got hold of a branch and swung himself gratefully up on it and lay still. As he lay there trembling, two men appeared and stood still.

'Perhaps it was a rat,' said the familiar voice. He directed his torch up the tree. Adu held his breath.

'Let's be fast. Where is it?' asked the other man. His colleague unwrapped something in a paper bag. As light fell on the objects, they sparkled. Then the man who held the light said. 'Look at that! This is pure gold; just look.' Immediately Adu knew who it was. He was so shocked he almost gave himself away with a yell. His fears vanished, replaced with curiosity and interest.

'Dig here—and let's be fast,' said the other voice. The man he knew handed the torch to his friend, and cleared dry leaves from a spot close to the edge of the grass and began to dig.

'Every three days we will move it until the matter is dead and forgotten in Buama.'

'It could take months.'

'Yes. But we can wait, even if it takes a year. We shall soon be rich.'

'They have more wealth than they need, that's why they bury their dead with gold when poor people like us have to toil day and night for simple daily bread.'

Then Adu understood. They were the grave thieves. But how could the man he knew be party to a deed like that? 'Let's go,' said the familiar voice. The man covered the freshly dug earth with dry leaves. Then the two men crept away. Adu waited until their torchlight had vanished before

126

he got down. He was just about to rush through the dark when a voice within him said: 'Take those precious things, boy.' He stopped and looked in the direction the men had gone.

'Quick—fool! Take them!' the voice urged him. 'If you took them you would be rich in a few weeks and then you could go away from your aunt for ever.'

Stealing? he asked himself.

'This is not stealing, fool, fool, fool. This is your chance. You didn't steal them, this is a gift from your father. You're not finished—your aunt lied to you—unless you don't take them.'

He walked towards the place and squatted by it. He felt the warmth of the freshly dug soil. But suddenly his friend Yaro was there again, in his mind, telling him it was wrong for him to have gone plucking Appiah's oranges without his permission.

Adu rose up and took to his heels. He ran through the tall grass. He found the way to the stream and ran towards the town.

The whole day Anane searched for Adu. No one knew his whereabouts. Anane had something to tell his friend; something serious, a secret that had been hidden for many years. He had heard this secret a long time ago but had decided to keep quiet about it. It involved Ama, and if it were revealed, both she and Adu would be affected. It was a secret about Goma.

But now he didn't care; he must tell Adu. What he had seen the previous evening had incensed him. When he went home, hatred for Goma filled his heart. As a personal revenge he decided to leak the secret he knew about her, the secret he had heard from his mother.

For the fourth time that day he went back to Goma's house. He met Ama at the gate. 'H-h-has h-h-he come?' Anane asked.

'Yes—just now.'

'Di-di-did your m-m-m-mother do any-anything t-t-to him?'

'No. She said...' Ama hesitated and remained silent.

'What d-d-did sh-sh-she say?'

'Well, it's all right, Anane. Adu is in his room.' Ama didn't want to repeat what her mother had said, although she thought about it. The woman had told Adu that she didn't care if Adu died in the bush or if he stayed there till the next day.

Ama went and joined the boys in Adu's room. Adu was eating boiled plantain and bean stew—the day's lunch that had been left over for him. He munched hungrily as he answered their questions about where he had been all day. He decided not to tell them anything about the grave thieves until he had informed Ofori about it.

When he had finished eating Anane said, 'Th-th-there's something I-I-I must tell you, Adu.'

'Tell me.'

Anane looked at Ama, who looked back. From the way Anane watched her, she knew she wasn't welcome to listen to their conversation, but she refused to leave. Ama had an itchy ear.

Anane waited but Ama sat down defiantly. Then he said, 'Ama, why don-don-don't you be a-a-a good girl?'

'What?'

'T-t-two minutes. Just ex-ex-excuse us for t-t-two minutes.'

Reluctantly Ama rose to her feet, made an 'I'll-get-you' face at Anane, and went out.

When she went back to the room she found the two boys sitting there looking so solemn that she was alarmed.

'What is it?' Ama asked.

'Oh n-n-nothing,' Anane replied.

Ama looked at Adu. By the way her friend was staring at her, she knew that whatever they had discussed concerned her. If not, why had they sent her away?

Anane got up. 'G-g-good night,' he said. 'To-to-

128

tomorrow at school.'

When he left Ama asked, 'What's wrong?'

'Nothing.'

'What did he tell you?'

Adu was silent.

'Please tell me.' Her voice was pleading.

'I can't.'

'Why not? Is it a secret?'

'No, not a secret. But I can't.'

The way Adu said it made Ama suspicious. She tried to guess but it was no use. Her curiosity grew. 'If it's not a secret, why won't you tell me?' Adu was silent. Ama was his best friend, but what Anane had revealed to him was too shocking to be true. 'No, it can't be true!' he said aloud.

'What?' Ama asked quickly.

'Nothing.'

Ama didn't like that and said so. She wanted to add, 'Will you treat me this way, Adu?' but she kept quiet instead. Adu was afraid he had hurt her, but he couldn't help it. He must think about this matter before telling Ama—that is, if he should tell her at all.

18

Ofori looked at the boy sitting before him. He could see how sad and lonely he was. The swollen eyes told of tears, a child saddled with too much grief for his age. But even more disturbing just now was the story Adu had told him.

In the last year Adu had moved from the primary into the middle school. The two school blocks stood side by side within the same compound. Although Adu now had a different teacher, Ofori, to him, was his teacher. It was Teacher Ofori who understood him and showed that he loved him. He could tell the teacher anything he wanted—and the teacher listened to him.

'Are you sure that what you're telling me is true, Adu?'

'It's true, sir. I heard them with my own ears and even though it was dark, I could see their faces because of the torch they had.'

Ofori gazed at the boy in disbelief. His mind whirled to his colleague in the school. He had seen him teaching, he had seen him in the headteacher's house, he had seen him on the football field. Then he focused on Adu.

'And you say you saw Teacher Afram?'

'He was the one holding the torch and he was the one who dug the place where they hid the things.'

'What about the other person? Have you seen him before?'

'No, sir, I've never seen him before.'

The news was shocking to Ofori. The crime had already received wide publicity not only in Buama but even in towns and villages in the district. In the primary school the matter had been discussed at staff level. Some of the bigger boys like

Charlie had been questioned about their activities in the town.

'This is serious, Adu,' Ofori got up, and paced the sitting-room. The boy wiped his swollen lips on his shirt sleeves. 'Adu,' Ofori turned back to him. 'Have you told anybody else about this?'

'No, sir.'

'Good. Let's go to the headteacher's house.'

'Sir, there's something else I want to tell you.'

'Okay.' Ofori sat down. Adu told him about the dream. To him it was obvious now who had killed his family. Wasn't it his aunt? And now she was after him. He could feel the spiritual battle now.

'Have you dreamt this way before?' Ofori asked the shivering boy.

'Yes, sir—two years ago, just before my parents died. In that dream the leopard almost got me.'

Ofori thought for some time. 'It's a spiritual battle, no doubt,' he said. 'But don't...' he hesitated. He wanted to dissuade the boy from calling his aunt a witch, or associating her with the leopard in the dream, but he refrained from it. The devil, he knew could use anybody who would let himself be used. What Adu had seen in his dream was not mere imagination. He took his Bible and read the first letter of John: 'You, dear children, are from God and have overcome them (the evil spirits), because the one who is in you is greater than the one who is in the world.'

Ofori explained. 'There's a constant battle between the powers of darkness and the power of light. Only those who are in Christ win this battle.'

'But,' Adu asked, 'why was the leopard unable to approach Yaro and me in the dream?'

'Yaro was a man of God. The leopard—the power of evil—could not approach you because it saw the power that was in the man of God. The verse I've just read to you says that the One who is in the children of God—that is the Spirit of Christ—is greater than the one who is outside—the spirit

131

of the devil.'

Ofori prayed for the boy. But Adu was scared. The truth of the struggle dawned on him only gradually. Why was he the target of this struggle? he asked himself. What wrong had he done? He still felt troubled, even as they left for the headteacher's house.

Motorway glared at the door for a long time. Seated in his big living-room were Ofori and Adu. They had just told him about Afram and the other thief. He pushed back his glasses and ran his palms across his bald head. Adu was sitting in the headteacher's living room for the first time. On the two walls opposite hung photographs of tractors ploughing large fields of what he guessed to be rice but which was actually wheat. The other picture was a poster of David killing Goliath the giant. Yaro had once told him the story. The picture showed giant Goliath heavily armoured but falling, with little David swinging a sling—the type that his father used to drive birds away. Yaro had told him how the stone from David's sling had made the giant's armour useless and added, 'David went to war against Goliath in the name of the living God and defeated him. No matter how small or big you are you'll win your battles if you battle in the name of the living God.'

'Let's inform the chief about it' Ofori suggested. Motorway thought for some time and then said, 'Isn't there a way to prevent this from public hearing?'

'How could we do that?' Ofori asked doubtfully.

'Supposing—' Motorway began, but saw Adu looking keenly at him and stopped. 'Adu,' he addressed the weary boy, 'take this chair and wait outside there. We shall call you later.'

'Yes, sir.' Adu took the chair and went out.

The headteacher leaned forward and said quietly, 'It's important that he doesn't hear everything, Mr Ofori.'

'Yes.'

'And what happened to his lips?'

'He had a row with his aunt again. He has a problem at

132

home.' Ofori briefed him on Adu's relationship with his aunt.

'Poor boy. Now, I was saying, suppose we contacted Afram himself to find out...'

'I have thought about that. But what if he denies any knowledge of it?'

'And he's sure to deny it, Ofori, you're right. If we succeed in settling this matter, I tell you, Afram will have to be transferred.' Motorway was angry. He added, 'I suggest that we inform the chief, then secretly keep watch over the spot until we can catch them red-handed, otherwise there is no way of making Afram and his friend admit the crime.'

'All right. But first we should go and check it ourselves.'

Minutes later Motorway, Ofori and Adu were on their way to the stream.

They went to the chief's linguist. He was dark and tall, with a moustache that made him look fierce. His heavy eyebrows and thick lips caused a chill within Adu. He wore a fading *kente* cloth with the folds gathered upon his right shoulder as he was a left-handed man. Left-handed people, it was said, were hot-tempered but cowards. This man was the opposite: he was known to be calm, patient and courageous. Behind his ferocious appearance was a man of wisdom. People of Buama said he was the strongest man in the royal family and that he virtually ruled the land. People who wanted to talk to the chief must first talk to the linguist.

Teachers were important people in Buama, looked upon with respect even by elders. The chief's linguist was happy to see the headteacher.

'What brings such honoured men to us today?'

'We have some important news for the chief,' Motorway began, 'and we thought the sun should not go to sleep until the chief has heard it.'

People often came to the chief's linguist with trivial matters, some of which never reached the chief. He thought

133

that he should perhaps listen to this one and quench it, as he had done to so many matters. 'What is it?' he asked.

Motorway turned to Ofori and asked him to speak. Ofori began to tell Adu's story, how he went down to the stream in order to run away from his aunt. When Ofori said that Adu had seen where the thieves who broke into the royal graves had hidden their booty, the chief's linguist gave a shocked and excited shout. The theft had brought unwelcome attention to his position as a key man in the royal family and there had been subtle criticism from those who wished his downfall. If he were able to catch the thieves and retrieve the missing things, he would not only consolidate his position, and shame his enemies, but also win the chief's favour and the admiration of the people of Buama. Here, then, was honey about to drip onto his tongue; he must open his mouth.

'Are you sure that what you're saying is true?' he asked.

'It is, Linguist,' Motorway replied. 'We have gone to see the place where they buried the treasures.'

The linguist nodded calmly, hiding his inner excitement. He asked, 'Do you know, Headteacher, that rumours which stray into the chief's ears are punishable by a heavy fine if they are found to be false?'

'I know. But we've been to the place and the freshly-dug earth is visible.'

'Supposing we dig the place and find it to contain nothing, or something that has nothing to do with the stolen items?'

'We've thought about that, Linguist,' Ofori replied. 'We suggest an ambush. People should be sent to watch the place.'

'And if it takes a whole year before the thieves return for their things?'

They had not thought about that. Adu spoke out for the first time, 'I heard them say they would return for the items in three days' time to change their hiding-place.'

The linguist appeared convinced. He agreed that he would provide men to keep watch that very night. But something else was worrying Motorway. He was about to speak when the linguist asked, 'Shall I tell the chief about this?'.

Ofori answered, 'We would rather that you waited until the thieves are caught.'

'All right, go and get ready. Be back here before sundown and take my men with you.'

'May I say this, Linguist?' asked Motorway. 'The question you asked a while ago about whether we knew what is buried is important. You're right, we cannot guarantee without doubt that the hole contains the items. We may catch the men, but if the things they buried are not the chief's properties, what will happen?'

'I've appreciated your efforts, my friends,' the linguist said, rising up, 'if it all turns out to be false, since you said I should not inform the chief, I'll treat it as nothing. We will forget about it.'

'Thank you,' Motorway said, relieved.

Ofori was almost trotting. He was eager to get to Beckie's house. Their appointment had almost been ruined by the incident with Adu. He hoped that Beckie would still be at home. When he got there he decided to play a trick. He opened her door slowly without knocking. Beckie was there, facing her open window. She heard the door open and did not turn to look. She knew who it was. She had seen him from the window.

Ofori stood behind her for some time, expecting her to turn and look at him. But she didn't. Ofori took advantage of this to admire her. He was about to ask Beckie to be his wife.

Beckie turned. Ofori had been smiling, but Beckie looked serious. For a brief moment the two lovers looked into each other's eyes.

'You did a good thing,' Beckie said, looking at Ofori with the same serious expression.

'We had a big matter that made me leave in a hurry,' Ofori explained. 'I thought I would come soon...'

135

'Oh, a big matter! I see. Then you should have told me yesterday, when you asked me to wait for you, that it wasn't to hear anything that was a big matter.' Her anger showed in her flashing eyes and in the tightness of her lips.

'It was to hear a big matter, Beckie,' Ofori said, approachng her, 'a matter bigger than you're prepared to hear.' He held her by the waist and drew her close. Beckie did not resist.

'I love you,' Ofori said. Beckie just looked at him. 'I said I love you.' Beckie remained silent. Then Ofori saw that her eyes were full of tears. Ofori took her in his arms.

'Beckie, I love you, and I want you to be my wife.'

Beckie sighed. Gently she unclasped his hands from around her hips and went to sit down. Ofori remained at the window, looking out.

'Sit down,' Beckie said. Ofori turned to look at her but kept standing by the window.

'Will you marry me?' he asked.

'Where were you?'

'We have a big case at hand, Beckie. I was on my way here when Adu came to me, claiming that he saw two thieves last night whom he thought were the grave thieves.'

'Really?'

'Yes, and guess what! We went to the headteacher and together we went to where Adu saw them bury the treasures. From there we went to the chief's linguist to report it.'

'You did all that?' Beckie said slowly.

Ofori nodded.

'I lost my temper,' Beckie spoke the words softly and slowly. 'I'm sorry.' She fell silent.

'Beckie,' Ofori said again. 'I asked you if you would marry me,' Ofori waited. Beckie rose up slowly and went and stood by the window. There was a long pause.

Beckie said, 'Yes.'

She said it very softly, but Ofori heard it.

The people of Buama were about to go to bed that night

when an unusual noise was heard from the centre of the town. The sound suggested that a mob had hurriedly been convened. Adu thought he knew what was happening. He rose up and went out. People were rushing from their houses towards the chief's palace. Adu followed them to the chief's compound, just in time to see Teacher Afram and his colleague being shoved into the guardroom.

While people asked what was happening, Adu nodded and went back to the house.

Everybody in Buama waited for the day of judgment with eagerness. The chief's courtroom was packed to capacity, with more people standing outside, and craning their necks to catch a glimpse of Afram the school-teacher and his friend. Both had done the abominable thing in Buama. Although the people had heard of graves being broken into, that was news from distant lands, it did not happen here in Buama. This was the most grievous offence ever committed on their own soil.

But many were disappointed. They were expecting a prolonged trial in which arguments would go back and forth, to try to find out the details of the crime. But instead the chief's linguist addressed the people in the chief's compound: Teacher Afram and his friend, he told them, had admitted their guilt. The chief and his elders had agreed to hand the matter over to the police. That was that.

As the crowd dispersed to their homes and working places, some were indignant. They wanted to see the culprits punished according to the traditions of the people. They were sure the police would find a way of freeing the thieves. 'I'll not be surprised,' one elder said to another, 'if tomorrow we see those two men roaming about here as free men.'

19

The events of the past week plagued Adu's heart. Too many things were happening within a short time. What worried him most was the secret that Anane had told him about Ama. Every time he thought about it he felt like crying. Ever since he had looked at Ama with sorrowful eyes. Anane had told him not to inform her, but there was no way he could keep quiet.

Yet he was scared of telling Ama. What would become of her if she got to know this? What would his aunt do? Perhaps she would kill him this time. Since Anane said it was his mother who had gossiped about it in his hearing, how would it affect the relationship between Mansa and his aunt? Now he began to understand why his aunt and Anane's mother were so close: they shared a big secret.

Slowly he got up from behind the back corner of the house. He had been sitting there all evening since supper time reflecting on these things. On his way into the house he met Ama.

'Is that Adu?' Ama called. 'Where have you been?'

'Ama!' Adu said, 'I've been looking for you. Come. There is something I have to tell you.'

They went back to the place where Adu had been sitting.

'Ama,' Adu began, 'there's something I should tell you. I didn't want to tell you, but...' He stopped.

'Is it something serious?' Ama asked.

'Yes.'

Ama became more curious. 'What is it about?' she asked. But Adu's courage failed him again. He could not not reveal the secret after all.

'I'm sorry, Ama; can I tell you tomorrow? I promise.'

Ama felt disappointed. She rose up and entered the house without saying a word to Adu. As soon as Ama went in Goma knew something was wrong.

'What is it?' She asked. Ama kept quiet.

'I'm talking to you, Ama,' Goma insisted. 'What's the matter?'

'Nothing, Mother. I was just thinking.'

'Thinking about what?'

Ama was silent.

'Come here.' Ama walked over to Goma. The woman coaxed her.

'It's Adu,' Ama finally said.

'He said he had something to tell me but he seems to be afraid to speak. He's making my heart beat.'

When the last word was out, she regretted it. This could get Adu into trouble.

'Why did he refuse to tell you?' Goma asked Ama.

'I don't know.'

At that moment Adu came in. He was heading for his room when he heard his aunt call.

'Come here, Adu.' Adu went and stood before his aunt.

'What is it you say you've got to tell Ama?'

The question rocked him and his face showed it. This was the last thing he would have expected Ama and her mother to discuss. He quickly pulled a fast one on his aunt.

'Aunt,' he said, 'it's about a test they did in class this week. I hear Ama scored the highest marks.'

Goma looked at her daughter's face to ascertain the truth. A faint smile came to Ama's face. Turning back to Adu, Goma said, 'Then why didn't you tell her? Why did you make it seem as if it was something dreadful?'

It was dreadful, Adu thought, but he remained silent.

'Go,' Goma said. Adu walked away.

If Goma was satisfied with the reply, Ama wasn't at all. It certainly was true that she had scored the highest marks in the geography test, but that was old news now and anyway she knew about it. She knew Adu had hidden the truth and that made matters worse.

Later, when Goma was busy with other things Ama slipped into Adu's room. 'Adu, why are you doing this to me?'

'All right, Ama, this is final. I can't tell you tonight but I promise to tell you tomorrow.'

Adu kept his promise. They were on their way to school in the morning when Adu said, 'I don't know how you'll take this, Ama, but they say...' He hesitated, 'they say my aunt is not your real mother!'

Ama's eyes flashed. She looked stupefied and stood rooted to the ground. Then, to Adu's surprise, her body relaxed and she laughed. For a moment no one spoke. Ama searched Adu's eyes and the corners of his mouth to detect confirmation of the joke she had just heard. She found none. Immediately her smile vanished and her body stiffened again. 'What did you say, Adu?'

'Anane told me. He said he overheard his mother and another woman discussing you and my aunt. He heard that you are not my aunt's real daughter. When later he asked his mother...'

Ama's body was shaking. The books she held dropped and scattered under her feet. Beads of sweat formed on her brow. Adu had mustered all his courage to reveal this, but now he stood there helpless.

'Is it true, Adu?' The calmness of Ama's voice strangely contradicted her shaking body.

'I hope it is not true, Ama.'

Ama looked away from Adu and stared with tear-filled eyes at the ground for a long time. Then slowly, forgetting her books and Adu, she turned back towards home.

'Where are you going?' Adu called after her. She did not reply. Adu bent down to pick the books. When he looked up again he saw Ama running towards home. He decided to follow her. He didn't regret revealing the secret to her. He

140

didn't fear the consequences from his aunt. He had only one thought: to keep an eye on his friend Ama and to be near her.

Ama ran as fast as she could, her heart pounding loudly. On the way she changed her mind—she wouldn't go home yet. Instead she dashed into Mansa's house without stopping at the gate and came face to face with the woman. Mansa was alarmed. She dropped the basket she was holding.

'Ama!' Mansa said and placed her hand upon Ama's shoulder. She saw that the girl was crying. 'What's wrong, Ama? Is your mother at home?'

'Anane's mother,' Ama began. She wiped her eyes in order to see clearly, 'Is it true...' she stopped. Mansa got the hint and began to panic. She was sure someone had broken the secret to Ama. 'Is it true,' Ama went on, 'that my mother is not my real mother?'

The woman betrayed herself by placing her palm on her wide-open mouth.

'Who told you?' Mansa asked, trying to compose herself. But it was too late.

'So it is true!' Ama yelled and began to cry aloud. Before Mansa could get hold of Ama she was already gone. Mansa went back to her house, shaking. She knew her son must have leaked the secret; he had been there when she had talked to the other woman about it. Or could it be the woman who had betrayed her in this way?

But at the same time Mansa felt calm about it all. Ten times and more she had suggested to Goma that she should tell Ama she was not her real mother. But Goma had always refused. Perhaps this was the only way Ama could know the truth about herself.

When Ama got to the house Goma was there. Ama stood close to her. She stared at Goma for a long time in a manner that both confused and alarmed the woman. In bewilderment the two watched each other. Ama's body was still shaking; her eyes were already red with tears. As

141

Goma looked at her she saw anger and something else she could not immediately identify.

Softly Goma said, 'Ama.'

The girl did not reply. She looked at the woman sitting before her. At once she realized that there was no resemblance between herself and the woman she had been calling 'mother'. Physically, in character, and in temperament they seemed to be miles apart.

'Ama!' Goma called again as she saw the girl's eyes sizing her up and down. She rose to her feet.

But Ama turned away and began to cry. She cried so hard that Goma was confused. She forced the girl into her room and looked on helplessly as Ama threw herself about, refusing to be comforted. At that point, Adu arrived at the house. Quietly he entered his room and locked the door. Then he listened.

'Oh mother, mother, mother!' Ama cried.

'I'm here, Ama. What's the matter?' Goma was disconcerted.

'My mother! Oh, where are you?'

'Look at me, Ama. Are you sick? Can't you see me? What's wrong?'

'My mother! I want my mother!'

'You're sick, Ama. What has gone wrong? Is your head aching? Let me give you some medicine.'

'I want my mother; my mother! Oh, oh, mother, where are you?'

Then the reality hit Goma. Ama had heard something. She put back the tablets she was pouring from a small bottle and sat down.

'Tell me what you're talking about, Ama. Look at me.'

'I want my mother,' Ama shouted, and Adu could detect a change in the voice that demanded her mother; he knew anger had replaced the weeping voice.

'You want who?' Goma asked in a shaking voice.

Almost immediately Adu could hear yet another voice. Ama spoke with a calm and composure that sharply

142

contrasted with her previous freting.

'Is it true, that you are not my mother?'

The question dropped like steel upon the ground. Goma had no answer. Her fourteen-year-old secret was out and she could keep it no longer.

'Who told you?' Goma asked.

'Is it true?' Ama demanded to know.

Goma rose up, trembling. 'So that was what Adu said he would tell you?'

'This has nothing to do with Adu,' Ama shouted. 'Go and ask Anane's mother.' Then she broke down and wept bitterly.

'That treacherous woman!' Goma yelled. 'I'll teach her to keep her mouth shut!' So saying she stormed out of the room and headed for her friend's house. She soon returned. Mansa was not at home. Ama was still crying when Goma entered the room and closed the door behind her.

'Ama...look here, Ama.' The girl was so overtaken with grief, she turned to the only mother she had known.

'Stop crying, Ama, I'll explain all this to you.'

But Ama cried. 'Why didn't you tell me?'

'You don't understand, Ama, listen to me...' But Ama only cried harder.

Adu, full of anger and indignation, tiptoed out of his room and left the house.

20

The news flashed through town. It was Goma again. That lovely girl she always called her daughter was not her real daughter. Ama had no parents. She, too, was an orphan like Adu... The news kept spreading like bush fire in the *harmattan* season. Soon it became the talk of town, until various versions of the story were spread. Some said she had stolen the child from a hospital. Others claimed she had picked her up, abandoned on an incinerator. And still others believed that, being a witch, she had confiscated the baby from other witches when they meant to kill her. In Buama rumours often got out of hand.

At school Ama was bombarded with questions by her mates, who wanted to confirm what they had heard. Was it true? they asked. Did she ever see her own mother? What did she look like? But Adu tried to protect Ama from the prying eyes and ears. He looked for her and prevented her from answering questions. One particular afternoon they decided to miss the closing assembly to avoid the fuss. They walked home in silence.

Adu looked at Ama from behind as she walked ahead of him. In the two weeks that had passed, the girl had already lost a lot of weight. She had cried daily, often refusing to eat. Goma's consolation and apologies had so far fallen on deaf ears. Many people, including Mansa, had tried to offer their own consolation but Ama would not listen; she called all of them wicked for knowing her plight and yet failing to inform her. Her spirit was broken with dejection. Since Goma was not her mother, who was?

As if in answer to the question, they heard the train hooting. It had just arrived at the station. Every time Adu heard the train passing by he remembered the day he had waited for it to take his sorrows away. As he walked home with Ama that afternoon he was unaware of a visitor who had just arrived on the train, a visitor whose presence in Buama would bring both pain and joy.

'Ama,' Adu said, 'you know I understand how you feel. I know it. Every time I think about all this I remember what Yaro told me when my mother died.' He didn't expect Ama to say anything. 'He told me that God was able to change bad situations to good ones. You know that I have not seen any good situations yet in all my troubles. But something about those words, and the sincerity with which Yaro said them that day, calms my heart every time I remember it. I don't understand it, but I keep remembering it. My friend said that it was faith to believe what you could not see and once you believe that God can turn bad things into good ones, it really happens.'

Ama only nodded.

The two friends continued to walk in silence. Just at the entrance to their house Adu saw someone he thought he recognised. He stopped.

'Is that not Appiah from Susa?' His face brightened up, surprised at what he saw. Running ahead of Ama he soon got to the man who had already seen him and was waiting for him.

'Ee, Boye's father!' Adu exclaimed.

'Adu!' the man called.

Adu ran and embraced Appiah. Ama reached them with a forced smile upon her face. The sight of the man Adu often mentioned momentarily relieved the pain in her heart. She remembered the man vaguely from her visits to Susa two years ago. Appiah told them he had come to Buama for a few days to transact a land issue.

'I've been longing to see you, Adu,' he said. 'How are you?'

'I'm fine, Boye's father. How is Boye's mother and Boye?'

'Everybody is well and they send their greetings to you. I've just been talking with your mother, Ama, and she told me you were both in school.'

It was the biggest surprise of the day. They all went into the house. Goma was grateful to see Ama enter the house with her calmest face for many days. Soon Adu and Appiah were engaged in conversation. Adu asked about Mahama and Yaro, his friends.

'You didn't hear about Mahama?' Appiah asked the question in a way that shook Adu. 'He went back home to his people in the north.' That relieved Adu. He was not surprised that Mahama could not live in Susa after his beloved master and friend passed away.

'Yaro is also gone,' Appiah announced.

'Oh!' exclaimed Adu. Yaro always told him he would return home some day to become a pastor. But he missed his friend. As they talked, Appiah watched Adu closely. He was shocked to see Adu reduced to a skeleton. Appiah longed to meet him alone to find out what he had been doing. Perhaps tomorrow they could talk privately.

That evening after Appiah had left Adu began to recollect things about Susa. He wanted to cry, but he had long since learnt to bite his lips.

The next day Appiah had the chance he wanted. Adu visited him in his friend's house and they talked for a long time. Adu told Appiah about everything he could remember. Now Appiah understood why the boy looked the way he did. When Appiah saw Adu he remembered his father Nimo. It was he who had saved Appiah's wife years ago. Now he was looking for an opportunity to return this kindness.

'Adu,' he said, 'I've been thinking. I want to ask you something. Do you think you could live with us in Susa?'

This was unexpected. In all his hardships the idea of going to live in Susa had never occurred to Adu. He had visited that tiny village of his birth thousands of times, but only in his mind. Although he certainly missed the place—the people, the farms, the trees, the houses—he had never thought about going back to Susa. The idea was welcome. Yes, wouldn't that remove him from his aunt? While he thought about this he realized why the idea had never occurred to him before: his aunt would never let him go.

'If you want, Adu, my wife and I will take care of you. Boye, your friend, is there, and you could continue at your former school. Your father was so kind to me and although he is not here today...' Appiah realized he ought not to have delved into that subject so carelessly; Adu was sobbing. Now he waited for Adu to settle. While he waited he remembered that he must not make Adu feel the reason he wanted to adopt him was in return for his father's kindness. If he did, he knew the idea would be ruined for ever. Adu would never go with him on that basis.

'It's okay, Adu, you're not alone. Will you come with me?' Adu wiped his eyes and was soon composed.

'But my aunt will not agree,' he replied.

. If Appiah did not believe Adu, he soon found out for himself when he approached Goma with the matter later.

'You don't know what you're talking about, Appiah,' Goma shouted.

Appiah was very surprised because no woman had ever talked to him the way Goma did. But he was patient.

'You don't know what you're talking about,' Goma repeated. 'When you insist on taking Adu away, what are you trying to tell me? Do you want to say that you can look after my brother's son better than I can?'

'No, that's not the idea.'

'If that's not the idea, then what is the idea?'

'I'm just trying to show my appreciation of Nimo's kindness towards me —that's all.'

'That's what I don't understand. If you really mean what you're saying then I would have expected you to bring a bag full of money—not to take him away. Or do you think the bag of cocoyam you brought gives you the boldness to want to take him away?'

Appiah was quiet. He realized it was useless arguing with the woman.

'That's the way some people create enmity among themselves,' Goma continued. 'I don't want any trouble, Appiah.'

Appiah went away disappointed. Maybe he should forget the matter, he thought sadly.

The rumour circulating in Buama about Ama reached Appiah. He asked Adu.

'It's true,' Adu said, and filled in the gaps for Appiah, who listened with interest. While Adu narrated the story, Appiah was thinking hard. Adu stopped at one point and looked at Appiah; the man was far away.

'Why, Boye's father? Is it something?'

'Wait a minute, Adu. Who first leaked this story?'

'The mother of a friend of mine. The woman's name is Mansa. Why?'

'Have you looked at Ama carefully?'

'Yes.'

'Do you know that she doesn't resemble your aunt in any way?'

'Yes.'

Appiah sat pensively for some time. 'How old is Ama?' he asked.

'She's thirteen. I'm a year older than her.'

Appiah made a mental calculation. His face lit up. 'Do you know our landlord very well?'

'Which landlord?'

'Yeboah—the landlord of our village back home. Did you see him many times before you came here?'

'Yes.' Adu recollected him very well. But he sought in vain for an answer to the puzzle. Was Appiah trying to reveal something? Adu asked, 'Do you think the landlord knew something about this?'

In answer Appiah said, 'Let's look for the woman Mansa.'

'Ama, listen to me,' said Adu. 'There's something I have to tell you. Perhaps this news may be better.'

Ama sniffed and wiped her nose like a little child. Adu couldn't wait to tell her what he and Appiah had found out from Mansa. 'I know who your father is!'

'Huh?'

'Yes. Boye's father and I went to Anane's mother's place and she told us something interesting. I know your father and you have seen him before. He's a nice man.'

Ama looked at Adu. Was she supposed to believe this? 'Did you say you have seen him before?'

'Yes, and you have seen him, too. In fact you've shaken hands with him. He's the landlord of Susa, our village.'

'Is this true, Adu?'

Adu was silent. He was still trying to piece fragments of past events together. Now he looked at Ama and said, 'I want to believe that this is true.'

'I'll ask my mother,' Ama said, and got up.

'Your mother...' Adu began and stopped. Ama left him there and entered the house. She called Goma her mother. That was when Adu knew Ama was going to be deeply disturbed in tearing herself away from the woman she had known as her mother since birth. Adu knew that once again he had started a row between 'mother' and 'daughter'.

Goma sat still on a stool in her bedroom. Ama sat in front of her. Sadness filled Goma's heart. After keeping the secret so long she now had the opportunity to reveal the past to Ama; it was a past she would have liked to forget for ever. As she thought, she wondered whether to tell her everything. Would Ama understand the craving in her heart that had driven her to do what she did? Would Ama appreciate the years that she had loved and cared for her, the years of pampering as an only child? Would Ama really understand that she would probably be dead had she not taken her away?

Maybe she would understand, Goma decided. Maybe she would. Whatever the result, she felt she owed Ama an explanation. Moreover if she, Goma, didn't tell her everything, then someone else was sure to do it.

The scene of the accident came to her vividly as if it were only yesterday. Goma and her friend Mansa had been travelling together when the accident occurred. As sellers of beads and traditional bangles they had travelled a lot. Those were the days when women travelled far and wide to sell their beads. When trade was good they would go away for several days, spending their nights in villages and towns.

It was a tedious job, but very lucrative. Goma and her friend were not the only ones to do this kind of job. It was common among women who considered themselves strong and able to undergo the strains of constant travel.

On this particular trip, Goma and Mansa didn't intend to go that far. They were visiting only nearby towns like Kube, Abenase, Duapompo, Mante and Brobe, to collect their monies from debtors. But something happened that changed their plans.

They were on their way from Kube to Abenase. As the two friends chatted, Mansa kept complaining about her naughty children and how she hoped they would not grow worse while she was away. She had left them in the charge of her busy husband and her younger sister who was staying with the family.

Any talk about children touched a raw nerve in Goma. War raged within her as she brooded over her childlessness. She had often lamented to Mansa that if she had even one child she would be happy. And one of the reasons for her travels was the hope of finding medicinemen who might help her to have a child. Most of the money Goma got from trading went to pay for medicines and medicinemen. On this particular day Goma was once again assailed by the strong desire for children.

Goma and her friend were sitting at the back of the bus. At the front, a man stood up to sell his local medicine which he said could cure all diseases. Goma didn't see him. She was looking at a woman who sat in front just behind the driver. This woman held a two-month-old baby in her arms and was breast-feeding it. Goma wished a thousand times that she was this lucky mother.

She knew the mother all right. That woman was Susa, the wife of Yeboah, the landlord of the village where her brother Nimo lived. Goma had not known she was there until after the bus left the station. She would greet her when they reached Abenase.

The accident occurred suddenly. The driver was negotiating a sharp curve when the vehicle skidded off the road and somersaulted a number of times before landing in a deep ditch. The screams of the dying and the wounded filled the air. Some people had been thrown out of the vehicle alive and unscathed. Goma and her friend Mansa were among the lucky ones. Goma was actually beginning to run away from the scene of the accident when a sight wiped all the confusion out of her and brought her to a standstill. Lying on a thicket of thistles was a tiny baby who had also been thrown out of the vehicle. It was alive. The baby was the child of Susa. Goma looked around and discovered the baby's mother under the wreck. She was dead.

When Goma picked the baby up and placed it upon her chest, she had no evil intent. She wanted to help a tiny child. But when the child cried, the old longing grew in Goma's heart. A weird idea exploded into her mind: 'This baby is mine...my baby...stop crying...baby.' When she discovered that this was a baby girl, she immediately called her Ama. 'Stop crying, Ama.' So Goma had a baby.

'My friend, are you alive?' the voice came from behind Goma, who turned to see Mansa rushing from the scene of the accident.

'Yes, I'm alive...and...look at this baby, my friend.' She stared hard at Mansa who seemed to understand the woman's intentions. 'Let me take her away, my friend...her mother is dead...'

Mansa didn't look as though she liked the idea. But before

she said anything a vehicle came to pick up some of the victims. Goma and the baby and Mansa were taken to the hospital at Kube.

Just a few minutes later Goma and her friend sneaked out of the hospital. They found a place in a public park where they hatched a neat plan.

'Help me, Mansa,' Goma cried. 'This is my only chance.' She was desperate. Mansa raised an objection, but as Goma pleaded she relented. Sympathy overrode reasoning and blinded them to any consequences.

'I'll help you,' Mansa assured her friend. 'What shall we do?'

Ideas came to Goma in a flash. 'I'll take the child to the north where nobody knows me.'

It seemed a good idea to Mansa. 'But,' she asked, 'what explanation shall we give to people?'

People were not Goma's biggest concern, and she told Mansa so. People? Weren't those people the very ones who mocked her and called her barren and other insulting names for being childless? 'Forget about people,' Goma told Mansa. 'Whatever you do people will talk about you. Let me do what will be best for me and my child.'

But Mansa insisted that if Goma really wanted to keep the child she must concern herself with what people might say. And so they made the plan that enabled Goma to keep her secret. Goma and Mansa abandoned their trips in the south and went all the way to Salaga in the north. They rented a room in a quiet suburb. Two days later Goma left the child in the care of Mansa and returned to Abenase where she reported that she and Mansa had parted company in one of the towns—as they sometimes did when they were unable to sell their goods. Mansa would be away for five days.

Goma's biggest task at that point was to convince her husband. She told him everything. 'We must take this child: her mother died in the accident and this child was going to die, anyway. This is our chance to stop people from insulting us in public.'

152

'Are you sure we must do this?' her husband had asked, terrified that his wife could think up such an idea. But Goma was a strong woman; she knew how to get what she wanted. She made the man understand that what she was doing was in the best interest of both of them. She even added that if they got the child people would stop thinking he was impotent, as some had indeed said. Did her husband want to continue to be a laughing stock in the eyes of the people of Buama?

'How can this be done?' the man then asked. 'Nobody has seen you pregnant!'

Goma unveiled the plan which Mansa helped her to construct. Goma and her husband would go away on a transfer to the north for three years. By the time they returned the child would be just over three years old.

'The child will look older than the age we say she is,' Goma pointed out. 'But that will be all right. Nobody is likely to ask silly questions about her age.'

Goma continued her story. The very next day she told a few people that she and her husband had decided to travel out of Buama for a while. She went ahead to Salaga in the north, allowing her husband time to force a transfer from his work place. Mansa returned to Buama later and kept her mouth shut about the entire plan. Goma compelled her to accept a piece of her land as a gift to buy her silence.

Three years later, when Goma and her husband returned to Buama, people congratulated them for their child. They made no fuss about Ama's age. Only her brother Nimo called her to the village and reprimanded her for going away without his knowledge.

'It worked, Ama,' Goma told the girl who sat before her, whose life story she was revealing. She said all this so freely, it was as if she were telling somebody else's story. 'It worked,' she repeated. Then she added, 'So, Ama, you are really fourteen years old, not thirteen. You were born in the same year as Adu.'

All the time Goma spoke, Ama was crying. But Goma did

not stop: the girl deserved the full story. When Goma mentioned that Ama was the same age as Adu, she looked up. Goma expected her to say something, but Ama kept quiet. Slowly the girl rose to her feet and left the room.

21

No one knew when Appiah left Buama, but when he returned a few days later, it was obvious where he had been, for he came with Yeboah. His visit to Mansa had convinced him that the story was true. To Appiah no honour could be higher than to be the first man to tell the landlord that his long-lost daughter was alive. His main task was to make the landlord believe him.

Yeboah rushed to Buama with Appiah in disbelief. 'Can it be true?' he kept asking Appiah and himself. Doubts, excitement, and even sorrow criss-crossed his mind. That his daughter should be alive only reminded him of his wife Susa. 'What's coming upon me?' he asked himself. Over-presumption even nudged him to entertain a faint hope that possibly Susa could be alive somewhere in this world.

In Buama he couldn't wait to see the girl Ama. The opportunity came that same evening. Appiah accompanied Yeboah and two of his friends to Goma's house. The moment Yeboah entered the house something seemed terribly wrong. The air was charged with a strange feeling, as if the whole thing was false. A girl came out of Goma's room and stood still upon seeing him. Yeboah also stopped.

For the first time Yeboah looked at the girl; he saw certain physical features which he quickly attributed to Susa his wife. For a moment he felt like dashing forward to hug his daughter, but the girl turned away and re-entered the room. Yeboah and his companions stood by while Ama informed Goma that some visitors had come to the house.

When Goma came out and saw Yeboah her first reaction

was to retreat, as she always did whenever she came face to face with him. But now everything was different. There was nothing to hide. She stepped forward and said straight out, 'Please sit down.' Yeboah and the visitors sat down. But before they said anything Goma continued, 'I know why you came. Everything is now over, but we can't talk here; call me in the chief's house.' Yeboah heard it, but he kept glancing at Ama who was standing at the doorway to Goma's room.

When they went away Yeboah had the face of his daughter engraved in his mind. 'Just like Susa her mother,' he muttered. 'Just like her.' He was elated, but somewhere deep within he felt hidden sorrow reviving.

'I've already told the chief and the elders here that I didn't give birth to the girl,' Goma addressed the chief's linguist. She had been asked to tell the story of how she had salvaged the tiny baby. In the silence of the palace, before the chief's council of elders, Goma narrated the pathetic scenes again.

The elders ruled that, since they had heard from Goma's own lips that the girl was not her daughter, there was no case: Ama should go to her father.

'I know that,' Goma replied, 'but I'm reminding the elders that I saved the girl from death; she would surely have died if I hadn't taken her. For fourteen years I cared for her as my own daughter, provided her with everything she needed, took her to school...Ama lacked nothing in the house...'

'Let this woman know, elders,' Yeboah said, 'that my family and I highly appreciate what she has done. If she demands to be paid for...'

'I was not requesting to be paid,' Goma cut in. 'My request is this: Ama is grown, she's not a child any longer. Let the elders call her and find out where she would like to live: with Yeboah or with me.'

That request made Yeboah angry. 'Did you ever hear this before, elders? There's no way the girl is going to remain with her. Fourteen years of agony is enough for me. Too much thinking about how that little child vanished was sending me mad. Don't you think I can hold you for...' he stopped.

'For what?' Goma asked, anger welling up in her.

'How do we know that you didn't do something to my wife in order to have the child?'

'No, no,' the chief cut in. 'Don't go that far, Yeboah.'

The old painful agony was threatening to re-awaken and Yeboah would be glad not to relive it all over again.

'We cannot give the girl any option to choose between you and her father,' the chief continued. 'You did well to tell us all about the girl and to admit that Yeboah is her father. You could have concealed the truth till the end of the world...'

Goma bit her lips. Indeed she could.

'...Having met his own daughter,' the chief went on, 'Yeboah, who has not shown any reason why he cannot take care of her, will take her with him.'

That was the chief's verdict and it was final. The matter would have ended there but Goma stood up and said, 'And suppose Ama refuses to go with him?'

'If the girl says this,' the chief replied, 'bring the matter back to this court.' That was the final word.

'Ama, you're my daughter!'

The girl gazed at the man who held her hand. Was this her father? So this landlord Yeboah was her father. And why had all this been hidden from her until now? When they asked her where she would like to be—with Yeboah or with Goma—Ama had chosen to go with Yeboah, since Goma was not her mother. But now how could she tear herself away from Goma and go with this man whom she knew almost nothing about? If all this was true, that meant she had no mother...

Yeboah watched the girl sitting before him and knew her mind was far away. 'You're not listening, Ama; I'm your father. I'm sorry about what happened to you. You will come home with me and everything will be all right.'

...If she had no mother, then who was this woman that she was going to live with as step-mother? Would she treat her like Goma treated Adu? She had been told that Yeboah had other children: how would those younger brothers and sisters regard her?

'Ama!' Yeboah called and gently pressed her hand. Ama came to and peered at her father. 'You look afraid,' observed Yeboah. Ama nodded. Yeboah pressed her to him and tried to reassure her. 'You'll come with me, won't you?' Ama nodded, through a maze of disturbing thoughts. She raised her eyes for the first time and asked, 'How about Adu?'

'What about him?'

'What will happen to him?' Ama asked. Then she said, 'Mother is very wicked to him...'

Yeboah wanted to shout, 'Goma is not your mother,' but he held back. He knew it would take some time for Ama to get used to her new state.

'I asked Adu if he would like to come with me, but he said Appiah wants to take him away to the village.'

'No,' said Ama firmly. 'Adu must come with us.' Her own fear of going to the new house would lessen if Adu went with them. Adu was her close friend and he was an orphan—almost like herself. They needed one another for encouragement and support. Adu had always expressed the desire to get away from his aunt, here was the opportunity.

'His father was a friend...the hardest worker in the village. I'd be glad if Adu would come with us.'

'I'll talk to him,' Ama said.

She found Adu at home. He looked at her shyly. 'Here you are, Ama. I've been wondering where you were. Will you follow your father?'

'Yes. And he wants you to come with us. Please, Adu, come with us. It'd be good for us to go together. You know I don't know anybody there.'

Adu bowed.

'Why, Adu?'

158

How was Adu going to tell Ama that he had chosen to go with Appiah back to the village? Susa was where he was born and bred. Going back seemed the natural thing to do. Moreover, his heart was in Susa, where he would live in the familiar places again—close to his family.

Ama wanted to cry, but Adu tried to explain to her why it was necessary for him to go back to Susa. 'It's only for a while, Ama. Once we get settled I'll visit you often.'

Ama began to cry. Suddenly she stood alone. Once she had been a happy girl living with her mother, now she was thrown out like a fish on the dry land. She was being led away by a man who was her father but whom she knew nothing about, to a town that she had never seen, into a family that was a stranger to her, to face a baffling future. Yet all these would have been a little bearable if Adu had gone with her. But even Adu, the boy she was growing to love, was vanishing from her life. She had been sharing his lonely life, his pain and sorrows, his future—but now there seemed nothing to share any more. Was their time meant to end this way?

Adu walked fast. He was going to Teacher Ofori's house. News about the teacher's transfer from Buama was on everybody's lips. The news came to Adu like a jab in his stomach. If Teacher Ofori was going away from Buama, his own days in the town were numbered, whether his aunt allowed him to go with Appiah or not. He saw in the teacher his father and mother, and certain aspects of Yaro. If Ofori was leaving Buama then his own life must change. A way must be found to make his aunt release him. He must not be left alone when Ofori and Ama were going away.

He knocked on the door.

'Come in,' Ofori called. Adu walked in. Beckie was there, busily addressing many envelopes.

'Hey, Adu! You heard the news?' Ofori said.

'Sir, they say you're going.'

'Yes, Adu. Your friend and teacher is going.'

159

Ofori didn't expect what followed. Without being told, Adu sat on a chair and began to cry. He did it so suddenly and sobbed so hard that tears stood in Beckie's eyes. She left the envelopes and placed her hands on Adu's shoulder. The touch seemed to make things worse. Adu's body shook.

'Stop crying, Adu,' Beckie tried to console him. 'It's painful for all of us. Is there something we can do for you before we say goodbye?'

It was bad for Adu but also for Ofori and his fiancée. Ofori felt sorry for Adu. The boy was like a younger brother to him.

Now as the boy cried Ofori's own heart broke. Adu had had his full share of grief. He began to see his departure as a harder blow to Adu than to the other pupils. Adu didn't get on with his aunt: he was always on the losing side. Sometimes Ofori had feared for him. But how could he help this boy? Perhaps he had already been doing it here in Buama, but simply being around to listen to him and to direct his life was not enough. Now that he was being transferred, what would he do?

'We've been thinking about you, Adu,' Ofori said. 'You know your friend Ama is going away with her father?' Adu nodded and wiped his nose. 'We thought her father would take you with him.'

'It'd be lovely, Adu,' Beckie said. 'You'd be close to your friend Ama.' Ofori and Beckie had discussed this but they were not sure whether Yeboah had thought of it.

'Ama and her father want me to go with them,' Adu replied. 'But...' he paused. Then he looked at Ofori and added, 'I don't want to go with them.' The surprise on Ofori's face spoke for him. Adu explained, 'I'm going to miss Ama too much and I wish I could go with her, but, Teacher, I don't know her father very well and I don't know his town. My father told me a story about him—how his wife—Ama's real mother—died and what happened before he married again. Ama herself is not sure how life is going to be for her. I don't know...' he paused. 'If it were possible I would rather go back to the village,' Adu said with a tinge of helplessness at the end.

'Back to the village?' Beckie asked.

'Yes. There's a man who has come from Susa. He was one of my father's friends, and his wife and my mother were best friends. He came to see a friend here.' It seemed to Ofori and Beckie that Adu was about to tell them something and they listened keenly. Adu continued, 'When I told him about all that I've gone through he asked me if I wanted to go back to Susa and live with him.'

Ofori looked at Beckie and they both nodded. All at once this appeared to be the solution to Adu's predicament. It was certain Adu would find no happiness with his aunt. Going away with Ama and her father would have been a fine option if Adu had had no objections. But if his own choice was to go with his father's friend back to the village where he was born and raised, they would give him their support.

'But my aunt has refused to let me go with him. She said I would leave the house only if she was dead.'

Ofori knew of Goma's power over Adu. She could wedge herself between Adu and progress, unless she was restrained. He felt strongly that Goma, having abused the simple trust to protect the dignity of her own brother's son, had also lost the privilege that went with this responsibility: the privilege of exercising authority over another human being. He saw Goma's threat to keep the boy against his will as undeserved.

These thoughts reminded him of something he had been withholding from Adu. He must tell him now. 'Adu,' he said, 'the chief has been thinking about you.'

As far as Adu was concerned, the sooner the case was over the better. People congratulated him for his heroic deed in retrieving the chief's treasure, but the weight of having brought two people to prison was heavy on him.

'The chief is thinking of rewarding you, Adu,' Ofori informed him. 'He asked me if there was anything you want him to do for you.'

Adu smiled. 'Can he help me to go away from my aunt and follow Appiah back to Susa?'

'Yes,' said Ofori. 'I think so. I'll ask the linguist about this.'

'When I left her Ama was crying. She's been crying since she heard that my aunt is not her real mother.'

'Naturally, Adu,' Beckie said. 'She has been placed in a difficult situation. I feel for the girl. I don't know what she will do.'

'Would it be all right for the chief to let us both to go to Susa with Appiah?' This unexpected request threw Ofori and Beckie off balance for a while. It was Beckie who spoke. 'It's a delicate issue, I think. Besides, do you think Ama will like Susa in the way you do? She has lived with your aunt for fourteen years here in Buama; she scarcely knows Susa the way you do—you were born and brought up there until two years ago. Well—I don't know.'

'This is a sad matter,' Ofori let out his feelings. 'It's so unfair for one person to throw two young lives into this chaos.' After a pause he continued, 'Beckie is right, Adu. But I'll mention it to the chief's linguist.'

22

When Adu left, Ofori and Beckie talked about the boy. Earlier on, the two of them had agreed that they would adopt Adu if need be, but now that an old friend was going to take him to his home village, they decided to drop the plans. That day Ofori went to see the chief's linguist.

'There is something that the boy wants,' Ofori began. 'If the chief would step in, he would be happy.'

'What is it?'

Ofori told him about Appiah. The linguist had already been informed about Adu. The chief himself knew all this. 'Has the boy expressed the desire to go back to the village?' the linguist asked Ofori.

'Yes. He said he would prefer that to the situation he is in.'

The linguist thought for a moment and then said, 'I'll tell the chief about it. The boy has done a lot for us and if that is what he wants he will get it.'

Adu's last day in Buama was a mixture of grief and relief. Appiah and Yeboah purposely arranged for Adu and Ama to leave the town on the same day: he to the village and she to her father's home. Everything was set for Adu's departure to Susa, the village of his birth. The chief had not only prevailed over his aunt to release him but had also bought him presents to take with him. It was a Saturday morning and Adu was on his way to Ofori's house. The school had organized a special farewell meeting for him and Ama the previous evening. But Adu also desired a closer farewell with Ofori and Beckie. He would soon see Susa again, the village he was sure he could never tear from his memory. This, coupled with the thought of leaving his aunt, brought him the relief he dreamt of.

Ofori was at home. One look and Adu could tell that his teacher was also getting ready to leave Buama. There were books and old packing cases in the yard.

'Adu!' Ofori called when he came out. He saw his young friend wearing a new shirt and shorts with sandals to match, some of the items the chief had bought for him. 'You look handsome, my boy. Don't say you're already on your way.' Ofori tried to sound as informal as possible to relieve the tension he could sense in the boy, but he knew that it was going to be a hard departure. Beckie came out of the house and saw Adu. One look at him and her heart sank. Even though things seemed to be working out well for him she could still see a very lonely boy. 'So!' Ofori started. 'Are you ready?'

'I'm ready, sir. I just came to say goodbye.'

That was all his heart needed in order to pour out the tears he was suppressing. Adu tried to hold them back but they flowed stubbornly. Beckie could not hold back her own tears.

'Don't worry, Adu,' Ofori said, 'we shall meet again. When you go, try and be a good boy. Don't let anybody find any fault with you. Be obedient to your new parents and the people of the village. At school respect your teachers and work hard. You remember the story of David Livingstone from your reading book, don't you?' Ofori began to quote, "although his father and mother were poor people, he worked hard at his books and became a doctor..." This was a direct quotation from a history book he often read with his pupils. Adu listened with his head bowed. 'Never forget what your friend Yaro taught you. You'll find him in the village, and if you do...'

Adu shook his head. 'My father's friend told me Yaro has left the village now.'

'I see. But I know the things he taught you about God still

remain in you, because you often told me about him: remember them. Don't forget what you've learnt here also about faith in God.'

Adu nodded.

On impulse Ofori added, 'As you know Beckie and I have been transferred together. In three months time we shall be married...' he paused to look at Beckie. Adu followed his gaze. All three smiled. 'In three days' time we shall leave Buama for good. Adu, in case of any difficulty, let us know. Beckie and I are willing to help you. Do you understand?'

'Yes, thank you.'

'Here's our address,' Beckie said, giving Adu a piece of paper. Ofori added, 'Don't fail to write to us and tell us how life is treating you in Susa.'

Adu took the paper and wiped away his tears. He lifted his head and looked at the faces of Ofori and Beckie; he saw husband and wife. Surprisingly, he smiled. Ofori and Beckie smiled too. They each embraced the boy and the goodbye was complete.

'We'll be at the train station to see you off, Adu,' Beckie said as they led him outside. Adu nodded. Ofori and Beckie stood there watching as the boy walked slowly away from them. Then they saw him raise the sleeves of his shirt to wipe his eyes. Adu turned and saw Ofori and Beckie standing where he had left them. They waved at him and he waved back.

When Adu got home he hastened to his room to complete the packing of his few belongings. But to his surprise it was done. He saw the bag containing his clothes and other personal effects and a carton that held books and other things. His mattress bed was bare and the pictures on the wall were gone. Even his machete was not in the corner where he normally left it; he saw it sticking out of the carton. He knew it was Ama who had completed the packing for him. He was still looking round his empty room when Ama walked in.

'Where were you?' Ama asked.

'I went to say goodbye to Teacher Ofori. You packed these things here?'

'Yes.'

'Thanks, Ama.'

They were silent for some time. Then Ama said casually, 'So you're going, Adu?' Adu looked at his friend. He had no words with which to say anything.

'Will you remember me, Adu?' Ama asked.

'I cannot forget you, Ama. I couldn't have survived in this place without you.'

They were standing face to face. Tears stood in their eyes but they held back from crying. They had cried too much already. But, overcome by grief, they began to cry silently. They tried to stifle their sobs but that only kept them crying. Suddenly they fell into each other's arms in a long hug. Then they sat down to console one another. That moment Yeboah and Appiah arrived. Goma was in the compound but after the men had greeted her, she entered her room.

'Are you ready, children?' asked Appiah at the doorway. Adu answered for both of them. They were ready.

In the compound Ama hesitated. She looked at Goma's door which was open. She put down her bag and entered the room. Goma was sitting lost in thought on a stool. Ama stood there for some time and then said softly, 'We're going.' Goma didn't respond. 'We're going,' Ama repeated. Goma looked up and nodded. Then she rested her head in her palm. Ama saw, for the first time, that Goma's eyes were wet. That moment Ama felt sorry for her. She was still standing there when a hand fell gently on her shoulder. She turned round and saw Yeboah. 'Let's go,' he said.

They all left for the train station where many people had come to see them off. Teacher Ofori and Beckie were already there. Anane had helped to take their luggage to the station. It took a little time for Adu's train to arrive. When it did, he detached himself from his friends and took his seat beside Appiah in the coach. Ama and her father had to wait for their train to arrive. Some of the people were waving as Adu's train crawled out of the station. Others stood still. Adu searched for Ama, and saw her father holding her hands. He waited for her to turn and wave but she didn't. The train pulled out of the station and soon all the people were far away.

23

The train pulled up at Susa about an hour later. There was the village again! Adu looked through the window and saw the Susa train station and people waiting patiently on the platform. Memories began to unfold in his mind as the train came to a stop. He got up and took Appiah's bag as well as his own things.

'Give me this and take the two bags,' Appiah said, taking the carton from him. When they got down Adu saw someone running towards them. He looked carefully. Yes, it was Boye, his old friend. Boye himself had not seen Adu. When he did he was amazed and stood still to make sure his eyes were not deceiving him.

Suddenly he shouted, 'Hey, Adu. Adu!' The two friends embraced.

'Adu!' Boye was not yet over his surprise. 'This is like a dream!'

'It is a dream, Boye!' Adu said and the two boys laughed so loudly their happiness infected those who watched.

'Father, what kind of trick is this?' Boye turned to his father. 'You were going to bring Adu and you didn't even tell us!'

Appiah only laughed. He was glad of the unexpected reception for Adu. He was glad to see the boy laughing and talking excitedly.

When they reached Susa Adu was surprised. It looked smaller than he remembered. There was the house he and his parents had lived in only two years ago. Memories rushed through his mind and settled upon his heart.

He quickly ignored his pounding heart and parched tongue and began to look around him. Boye was already ahead of them. He entered his house before Adu and Appiah. Someone appeared at the entrance; it was Boye's mother. The woman ran towards her husband and the boy who followed him. Ignoring Appiah, she embraced Adu with a cry of surprise.

'Adu, my son! Adu!' Boye's mother hugged Adu and lifted him high. Adu was overwhelmed with a mixture of joy and grief. He looked at the woman who had just called him son; she hadn't changed at all. She was still Boye's mother, the woman he knew.

The woman was quick to notice that Adu had grown thinner in the last two years.

The little commotion attracted other people; they flocked to see Adu in Appiah's house. They came in to sit and to chat. They asked Adu about Buama, about life there and about his aunt. They asked him about school and his friends. The rest of that day was spent talking and greeting. Everybody was surprised to see Adu once more.

Before Adu had time to go out of the house again it was already dark, save for the full moon that roamed in the trees. He stood at the entrance of the house and studied the moon. Did that also remind him of long ago? Didn't it remind him of the time when his mother told them stories? Under the full moon Susa used not to be as quiet as on this night. In those days, he recalled, boys and girls played all kinds of games in the moonlight. He was still reliving those days when Boye found him outside.

'Boye,' Adu spoke out his mind, 'tell me, why is the village so quiet on a night like this when the moon is so bright?'

'Ah, Adu,' Boye answered, 'things have changed. Susa is no longer what it used to be. All the friends we used to play with are gone. Two families moved away only last month.'

'Do you still go bird hunting?' Adu asked.

'Sometimes, but not as we used to do, Adu. Things have changed. But now that you have come, well, maybe we'll do as we used to.'

That was not good. That night Adu's mind was more in Buama than it was in Susa.

The next day Adu had the opportunity to look round the village. Appiah had gone to town to contact the school authorities about Adu's return. If everything was all right he would continue with schooling immediately.

But as Adu went out, something told him a mistake had been made somewhere. The final blow came when he decided to go to his family's house. As soon as he entered he was hit by memories. There was nobody in the house. The family that had shared the big compound house had moved away a long time ago, he was told. Since then nobody had had the courage to move in. As he watched his father's door he had a feeling it would open.

There was his mother's room; it was locked. He could hear mice chasing each other in the room and dropping things from the ceiling. The house was deserted.

Mahama's door was open and he felt like entering. He resisted the urge and simply stood there surveying one place after another. His father used to sharpen his machete here; there was the shed where they kept the rice and maize. The kitchen was also open; he could almost see his mother and Yaa preparing the meals. After that they would sit down and eat and listen to stories.

Adu didn't know what he was doing to himself until he turned to go. The very act of going revived his thoughts. It was as though he was turning away from his parents. It was as if they were alive and only he was dead.

He found himself unable to leave, even though he had been in that house for over two hours. He turned back and sat on a stone close to his mother's room. He pictured his family going about in the same house where he sat now. He rested his head on his knees and the tears fell. Soon his whole body was wracked with sobs which he did not try to control.

'Where's Adu?' Boye's mother asked her son. He had no answer. 'I thought you went out with him?'

'No. I was in the room. I didn't know he went out.'

The woman had suspected it all the time. The night before, when her husband arrived with Adu, she had spent a long time thinking about the best way to keep the boy's mind off his grief. Susa was the wrong place for him. It was unfortunate that Adu had suffered at the hands of his aunt. But Susa was no substitute for Buama. The memories were too fresh and the events too close to keep his mind at peace. If it was hard for the adults, how did her husband think it would work for the poor child? The only thing in favour of his coming back to Susa was the poor treatment he had received at the hands of his aunt. But for that, she reasoned, it would be better for the boy to be away from this place. But she kept these thoughts private. She vowed to do everything in her power to make the boy happy.

Boye's mother knew where to check first for Adu. She went to the family's house and found Adu crying out his heart right by his mother's door. The sight saddened her so much that before she knew it she was crying with the grieving child. 'Adu, it's hard; Adu, it's all right. Let's go home.'

They went home. Adu began to understand why he had never felt the urge to return to this place. It was a place best to be visited with the mind, not in person.

When Appiah returned from the town his wife told him about the incident and added a piece of her mind. Appiah called Adu to his room and told him, 'It is only because you have just arrived, Adu. If you try to overcome the initial problem you'll soon discover that you can stay here. Try, Adu. I know how you feel; only try your best.' Adu said he would.

'Would you like to go back to your aunt?'

'No,' he replied sharply.

'So then, try and live with us. My family will take care of you and you have nothing to fear.'

171

But Adu had already made up his mind. That very night he called his friend Boye outside and revealed his plan to him.

'I must go away, Boye.'

'You must go away?' Boye's reply showed his surprise.

'Yes.'

'Why? You just arrived!'

'I know, Boye, but I can't live in this place.' Quickly, he added, 'I want you to do something for me, Boye.'

'But this doesn't sound nice, Adu. Why not wait for some days. I'm sure things will improve.'

'You don't understand, Boye. It'll not work. I've thought about this very much. Please just do this one thing for me. Some time tomorrow morning I'll leave. When I'm gone, please tell your father and mother.'

'Where are you going?'

'I'm sorry I can't tell you now, Boye, but later you'll know. Please just tell them I'm gone; I'll be alive and well. Tell them I certainly do appreciate their kindness. I'm sorry for this but it is for the best. Boye, I can't live here any more.'

The whole plan tasted sour in Boye's mouth and he told Adu so. But he promised to do as he requested.

The day broke slowly—almost too slowly for Adu. He had lain awake most of the night planning his escape.

Appiah had decided to go to the farm to visit his palms. He felt he should allow Adu and Boye to have their freedom before taking them to the farm, so he had left early.

Adu waited for some time after Appiah had gone and then started his plan. Boye's mother was still in the kitchen getting the morning meal ready when Adu took his travelling bag and vanished behind the house. Boye saw him going out and shivered.

Adu waded through the bush and then came to the main path leading to the town. He kept looking round to see if anyone was coming towards him or following him. Twice he saw people coming towards him and took cover in the bush till they passed.

He got to the train station just in time to see the early

morning train pulling away. He bit his lips for missing it. Now he had to wait for the late morning train which sometimes came around midday.

But he was determined. He entered the main hall of the passengers' lounge and sat in a far corner. He was hungry but too cautious to buy food. He didn't want to be stopped.

As he hid in the lounge he imagined what might be happening. He was almost sure by then that his absence had been detected and that Boye had broken the news to Appiah and his wife. He felt sorry to disappoint them but he knew he was doing the right thing. Susa was now an impossible place for him to live.

It was close to midday that the late morning train came by. He boarded it stealthily and hid in an obscure place in a third class coach. As the train hooted and snaked out of the station he knew in his heart that he would not see Susa for a long time. He relaxed.

An hour later he was in Buama. His only hope was to find Ofori and Beckie at home. Susa was no longer good and Buama held little hope. He didn't regret not going with Ama and her father. And he would never think of living with his aunt again. He hurried past the houses. People he met expressed surprise at seeing him. They thought he had gone to his father's village, and wondered why he was back so soon. He gave everybody he met a prepared reply and resisted their urge to stop for more questions.

The sun was blazing. The activities in Ofori's house were hectic. The tipper truck parked in front of the house was half full with his belongings. Some of his pupils were there to see that their teacher didn't lack help with his final packing. Some of them were there to see if there was anything left over from the packing. They went about their duty heartily, though once in a while a pupil stopped to stare at the beloved teacher. Ofori himself was busy sorting out what items to pack and what to leave behind. Beckie was with him.

'Take this,' Ofori told a pupil and handed him a broken

flower vase.

'That thing is cracked, dear,' Beckie protested, taking the vase from the boy. 'I doubt whether it'll survive the journey. Even if it did...Hey, Adu! Adu!'

Everybody stopped and turned round.

'Adu!' Beckie yelled again and dropped the vase. Everyone was speechless. Adu was standing at the gate. When Beckie called again he moved slowly towards her. His bag was hanging on his shoulder as he took those faltering steps towards his hope of survival. Ofori and Beckie had expressed their willingness to take him. Would they indeed do it?

'Adu!' Ofori called and held the boy's hand. Everybody looked on. 'What happened?'

Before Adu could answer he broke down and wept. Ofori led him to the room and tried to calm him down.

'What happened?' Ofori asked again and waited for the boy to wipe his nose and eyes. Adu shook his head and said, 'I couldn't, teacher. I can't live in Susa. Everything there reminds me of my family.' He sobbed. Ofori turned to Beckie and said, 'I told you, Beckie; I knew it couldn't happen.' Then he turned to Adu. 'Listen, Adu, Beckie and I have already discussed this. We'll take you with us. Do you understand? You'll make your home with us. Do not fear; God will keep you. He will turn your grief to joy.'

24

'I don't think she'll like to see me,' Adu said again and turned away from the piercing glare of Ofori.

'But,' Ofori said, 'do you want to see her?'

That was the question he'd feared Ofori would ask. It was the crux of the problem.

The problem, Adu knew, was in his heart. It was his heart that refused to forgive. He didn't even want to see his aunt, so to ask him to forgive her was asking for the impossible. If he could not even bring himself to say, 'Auntie, I forgive you for all the wrong you've done against me,' how could he think of saying, 'Please, Auntie, forgive me for all that I've done against you'? What wrong had he done against his aunt? The question was in his mind and directed at Ofori. Was he the one who had wronged his aunt? Wasn't it his aunt who had wronged him, by adding to the grief he bore?

But he dared not translate his thought into words.

The teacher and the pupil sat under a young palm tree in the compound of Ofori's three-room flat. The conversation, however, was between a man and his son. In the six months since they had moved from Buama to Nsupa, their new station, Adu did not see Ofori and Beckie as teachers but as parents. The newly married couple regarded Adu as their firstborn, and treated him as such.

Ofori was careful that what he was asking Adu to do would not be seen as a command or an instruction. If Adu said this was difficult, it must indeed be harder than the boy could convey, for this was surely the first time he had not spontaneously jumped at an opportunity to obey his new parent. Over the past six months, Ofori and his wife had found the boy easy to live with—'quite beyond my expectation, you know,' Beckie had told her husband just a few days before. They were particularly grateful that Adu really tried to live by what he said Yaro had taught him. They were happy that Adu no longer talked about his parents with pain.

The person he talked about more often was Ama. He hadn't seen the girl since they moved to Nsupa, and he said he missed her. The day he received a letter from Ama, Ofori and his wife knew at once that something unusually good had happened to their boy. He gave the letter to Beckie to read. It was obvious the girl had struggled to write, but she conveyed a message they were all glad to receive. Ama wrote that she was fine, and that her father and her step mother were proud and happy to have her. (Beckie was quick to notice that she said nothing about whether she herself was happy.) Discussing Ama aroused Adu's desire to visit his friend.

The person he avoided talking about was Goma, his aunt. Every time a reference to her came up in their conversation, Adu clearly showed his disgust. On the rare occasions when he talked about her it was with such hatred that Ofori knew something must be done. That was the reason for this afternoon's chat between father and son. 'I know this is difficult for you, Adu,' he said, 'considering all that you went through in your aunt's house. But let me ask you a question.' Adu looked up. 'Do you know that you've also wronged your aunt?'

The crease in Adu's forehead showed that the feeling he closely guarded was out in the open. His eyes asked the question, 'What did I do?'

'You hold something in your heart against your aunt. You hate her. You bear her bitterness and grudge because of all that she did to you. Am I right?'

Adu bowed his head.

Ofori dropped his bomb: 'Adu, you need to forgive her.'

Adu did not look up. It was true. But his aunt had started it all. When he followed her from Susa to Buama after the death of his family, what wrong did he do her? It was her brutality towards him that had made him hate her. It was not his fault.

Ofori said, 'I know you're thinking it was your aunt who started it all...' Adu looked up in surprise. How did Ofori know what he was thinking? Ofori went on, 'But whenever you do anything wrong, it's better to admit it and do something about it than to blame someone else. Always remember, Adu, that our relationship with God, which your friend Yaro told you about, affects our relationship with other people, no matter what they are like.' He paused. Could Adu understand all this? Sometimes he wondered what sort of boy this was —a boy whose mind was older than his body, who understood things faster than boys of his age. But then this boy had experienced in three years more than most adults go through in a lifetime. He might or might not understand everything that was told him now, but his peculiar situation demanded that he should be told and encouraged to take decisions that would help build his life for the future.

'As it is,' Ofori continued, 'we've all wronged God one way or another and need his forgiveness. But did you know that when God forgives us he makes it a condition that we forgive other people?'

Adu kept silent but he was listening. He recalled how Yaro once told him the story of a man who refused to forgive a fellow debtor and was punished for his wicked action.

Ofori looked straight at Adu and said, 'If you keep this bitterness against your aunt and refuse to forgive her, how can you expect God to forgive you?'

The words were sinking in. Adu's brow lost its crease, and his body became less rigid.

Ofori added cautiously, 'You've got to ask your aunt's forgiveness before she...' he stopped. 'Did you hear that your aunt is seriously ill?'

Adu nodded. Beckie had told him the night before. He

177

sighed, but it was a sigh of consent. He said, 'I didn't know that I had wronged my aunt. I'll go.'

Ofori said no more.

When it was obvious they would travel to Buama, Adu made a request. 'After Buama,' he said, 'can we please go on to Abenase to visit Ama and her family?' Ofori said that would be fine.

Mansa stared at the visitors and listened to their message. It was Beckie's idea that instead of going straight to Goma's house it might be better to see Mansa first. Ofori would have preferred to go through the chief. But Beckie insisted that it was better to approach the matter privately through Goma's friend than officially through the chief.

Mansa kept staring at Adu. 'And how are you, Adu?' she asked. Adu said he was fine. 'I can see that,' Mansa observed. 'It seems you like your new place—they're taking care of you well.'

'Tell us,' Beckie said, 'can you please lead us to go and see Goma? We thought it would be fine if you went with us.' Mansa agreed to go with them.

Goma was dozing in an old armchair in front of her room when Mansa led the three visitors into her compound. A young girl was sweeping around the kitchen area. It was she who first heard the sound of approaching footsteps and rose up to see who the visitors were.

'Auntie, we have visitors,' the girl announced, as she put down her broom, and scrambled for chairs.

Goma jerked up and glared at the unexpected visitors. When she noticed who they were she asked, 'What do you want?'

'Let them sit down first,' Mansa said and took the seat the girl had provided. She urged the visitors to do the same. Adu cast a quick glance around the compound. Not much had changed—except the presence of the girl, who, it seemed, occupied his former room. He had just seen her coming out of it, wearing a scarf. Perhaps his aunt had taken a maid to help her. Now he turned to see his aunt peering at him. For a split moment a chill ran through him: those eyes again!

But this time no bell sounded in him. He looked away from his aunt's gaze, but it was more out of respect than fear. Now he was confident that his aunt no longer had any powers over him. She could not destroy him: Ofori and Beckie had assured him of that. The powers of darkness could not harm him, because he had the Lord in his heart.

As Ofori narrated the reason for their visit Adu began to feel sad for Goma. She was a lonely woman, wasn't she? Goma was the last person left of his father's family beside himself. If the two of them were to die that would be the very end of Nimo's lineage. With that fact came the realization of something else: he was an orphan!

Quickly Adu shook the thought out of his mind. It sounded ominous to him—yet it was true that he had no father and no mother. But he did not want to think about this any more. He had come to understand that no child of God was ever an orphan. He had already decided to tear himself away from the crippling, gnawing feeling of loneliness that imprisoned him in the past. Why should what belonged to the past suddenly rear its head in the presence of his aunt? No: he rejected it. 'No,' he determined in his heart, 'I'm a child of God; I'm not alone.' It was a personal determination.

When it was time for him to speak, he stood up. He looked directly at this aunt and said, 'I...I'm sorry, Auntie, for all that I've done to you. I want you to forgive me...'

'What are you sorry for?' Goma cut in, piercing Adu with a gaze that bewildered the boy. She meant to cow him into submission and break him down. But Adu stood firm. There was no fear in his heart. Suddenly Goma shouted, 'I say tell me what you've done—and stop looking at me like that.' Adu was still standing and looking directly at the woman. For a brief moment aunt and nephew were locked in their gaze. Finally Goma looked away.

'I know why you people came,' she said, but her voice was

no longer harsh. 'You heard that I was sick, and you thought I was going to die. So you brought this boy to come and say words you've pumped into his mouth before I go.' She said that calmly.

No one spoke.

'I'm not going to die now, do you understand? The witches of Buama wanted me to die but God has not killed me yet...' her voice trailed off and ended in a tremble.

Ofori saw that the woman was not as ill as the report had said. Her words sparked a feeling of guilt in him. She was right. He had imagined—if that wild report was even half true—that the woman was in bad shape and might die. As he turned away from her eyes, Adu began to speak again.

'The words I'm speaking are my own words, Aunt,' he said. 'No one put them in my mouth...' Everyone sat up. 'I'm sorry about this, but I hated you. Because of what happened I didn't like you. I hated you...' He paused and then continued, 'But now I no longer hate you. I have nothing in my heart against you any more. I want you to forgive me...'

Goma was not looking at him. The silence was heavy and unpredictable. Then, as he studied his aunt's face, he saw the strangest thing. His aunt was wiping tears from her eyes.

Nobody spoke for a long time. It was Mansa who finally said, 'It's all right, Goma, my friend. The boy is sorry. Life is like that; it may seem bad today but tomorrow something good will follow. Adu is still your nephew, your own brother's son. He's just a child; he will grow up, and when he grows up, who knows, he may be the one to...'

Mansa stopped because Goma rose up and entered her room. When she came out again the tears were gone. 'Let's forget everything,' she said. Then, as if to prevent any further discussion, she added quickly, 'Where's Ama?' The question was directed at Ofori.

'We hear she's fine,' Ofori replied. 'But we don't know for sure.'

Goma sighed loudly. She bit hard into her lips. Her mouth twisted in regret, and she sighed again. But she said nothing.

Later, when the Oforis and Adu left Buama to visit Ama and her parents in Abenase, Adu felt that a heavy burden had been lifted from his neck.

Adu was impressed. He had been told that Abenase was a small town. But now he had seen the place he was impressed with its beauty. There were more trees in this town than in Nsupa where he lived now with the Oforis. He could not miss the yellow canary birds making so much noise among several of the trees as they wove their nests. They were a powerful reminder of Susa.

Ofori, Adu and Beckie were waiting in Yeboah's compound. When they had arrived, someone told them that the entire Yeboah family had gone to the cocoa buying yard where they were helping Yeboah's farmers to bag the dry cocoa beans.

The visitors did not have to wait for long before they saw someone running towards them. 'Adu, Adu, Adu...' It was Ama. She ran up to Adu and hugged him.

'Ama!' Adu began, but didn't know what else to say.

'When did you arrive here?'

'Just now. Go and greet Teacher Ofori and Miss Annan—sorry, Mrs Ofori.' Ama walked shyly towards her former teacher. 'Ama,' said Beckie, before Ama got to her. 'You look nice—how are you?'

'I'm fine, Miss Annan, thank you.'

'Now you should call me Mrs Ofori,' Beckie said. 'You look really nice, Ama. We were concerned about you.'

Yeboah, his wife, and two children came up to greet them. 'It's good to see you again, Mr Ofori. Ama has told me a lot about you. She kept telling us how you were going to marry her teacher...' Everybody laughed. 'Now,' Yeboah continued, feeling excited, 'you haven't met my family, have you?'

'No,' said Beckie. 'We're glad to meet the rest of them... We know Ama.'

'Yes, of course. This is my wife, Akos, and our two

181

children: Cobbie and Adjo... But please come into the room.'

Adu and Ama waited outside to talk. They shared all that had happened to them and compared feelings.

'You didn't reply to my letter.' That was Ama. Adu attempted an excuse, 'I knew we would come and see you soon. But I'll write to you when we get back. I promise.'

Later, when they were about to part company again, Adu said to Ama, 'I told you that you would be all right and that your stepmother would not be like my aunt.'

Ama's reply surprised Adu. 'My stepmother is very kind to me,' she said. 'She encourages me and calls me her daughter—just like my mother used to do...'

'Who used to call you?'

'My mo...I mean your aunt.'

The two friends were silent. Ama's mistake was not a light one. It would take some time to correct it. 'Let me tell you, Adu,' Ama said, 'since I came here I've dreamt about her more than ten times. I can't think of her not being my mother. I know my stepmother is kind to me...my father likes me...my stepbrother and sister are fine. But I still feel I'm a stranger here and that your aunt's place is where I belong...'

Adu took one look at Ama and knew the girl was serious. What could he say?

'Ama,' he began, 'it'll be all right. I felt the same when I went away with Teacher Ofori. There were times when I felt I was a stranger there. But I knew it was the best place for me. I know it will not be too long before you get used to this place.'

Ama didn't answer, but she knew that Adu was right.

Epilogue

Eleven years passed, almost too swiftly. On a lonely, newly tarred lane that ran through recently built public flats in Abenase, two friends strolled side by side. Dusk was approaching but they were not in a hurry to part. It was a quiet Sunday evening. Around them, a gentle wind stirred the young trees that lined the street. Not many people used this street of the suburb, and so the two friends had a place to themselves. Their only companions were the three-day-old moon, and a few bright stars, already in the sky. The moon and the stars seemed to walk up and down with them.

'I love the moon,' Ama said.

'Me, too,' Adu replied. 'It's beautiful.'

They strolled silently on.

'Do you know why the moon always appears in the evening with two or three very bright stars to accompany her?' Adu asked. Ama thought for some time and said, 'I wasn't taught that one at school.'

'Well,' there was triumph in Adu's voice and a smile on his face, 'the moon is the lady and the stars are young men. Every star in the sky wants...' He suppressed the laughter hiding in his cheeks.

'You cooked that one up,' said Ama, surveying Adu's face to confirm her suspicion. 'Who told you this?'

'My mother. She said beautiful moons never lacked stars to pursue them.'

Ama only chuckled. Silence overtook them again.

Adu had something to tell Ama this evening. He had kept it to himself for many months, since the pulse in his heart

183

began to nag him to it. This evening he must tell her. But there was no hurry. He took his time.

The smile he had tried to suppress returned, but it was not for the moon and her lovers; it was for himself. He couldn't believe that all this was happening to him—that he, once a child of grief, was no longer a child nor grieved. He had never thought he would be able to smile on life as he could today. Him? Of all people...? Eleven years ago he had taken those shaky steps into a future he knew nothing about. For eleven years he had tasted the kindness of a couple who became his parents: Ofori and Beckie. He had grown to love them, and their three children—especially the little boy who chose to call him uncle although the others called him big brother.

'Thank God!' He said that aloud. Ama heard it. She looked at him and asked, 'What for?'

'For everything. For everybody. For you, for me, for Ofori and Beckie. For your father and stepmother. For everybody who has helped us.'

'For Yaro!' Ama contributed.

'For Yaro—of course!'

Another spell of silence. Two people overtook them on the lane and hastened towards one of the flats. Dusk was fully here and the streets were well lit. A few fireflies sparkled on and off in the air, criss-crossing one another. But Adu and Ama were oblivious to them.

And for Yaro, Adu feasted on that thought. But for Yaro he would probably be dead. Yaro was the man who first taught him the steps of practical faith in God. He knew now that it was no ordinary thing Yaro had given him. Where would he be without the faith in God that sustained him in those fragile moments when he would otherwise have chosen death? As his faith had gained ground these past eleven years, he had begun to ask for something special for Yaro. Yaro was as lonely as Adu himself, a wandering man with no family, who insisted that God was enough family for him. Often Adu had prayed that God would give Yaro a family of his own. Now he smiled at the direct answer to his prayer; for

184

recently he had heard that Yaro had indeed married a young woman from his own tribe.

No, he had never thought that life could smile on him again, or that he could smile on life. But now here he was, a teacher. He loved Ofori and Beckie, and he loved their profession as well. After his elementary education he had decided to train as a teacher. He enrolled at a teacher training college for four years and after that began to teach in the primary school.

In all these years he had not broken contact with Ama. Something more than friendship had begun to grow between them as they matured into young adults. It was no surprise to Ofori and Beckie—or to Ama and her parents—when, two years before, Adu had asked for a transfer to Abenase. For accommodation he got one of the newly-built flats in this quiet suburb. Since he had moved to this place Ama had come to know the area as well as she knew the place where she lived with her parents.

'Perhaps I should move into one of these flats,' said Ama. It was a deliberate attempt to break the silence.

Adu smiled. 'Exactly why do you want to come and live here?' He asked, in a voice that implied he knew the answer.

'Who said it's because of you I want to come here? I just like the flats. Can't you see they are beautiful?'

'I know.'

They both laughed.

'Besides,' Ama began, and stopped.

'Go on. Besides?'

'Nothing.'

'No, seriously, I want to know.'

'Do you know how old I am? At my age, don't you think I deserve my own flat?'

'Oh, yes, of course!' The mocking tone in his voice was still there.

They strolled on. More stars had appeared to woo the moon, but the evening was still young.

There is no condition that is permanent. Adu recalled a

favourite saying of Teacher Ofori. He didn't need anybody to tell him that was true. If not, he would be a grieved child still. But the years of grief were over. Through the pains of loss and deprivation he had learnt that with God all things are possible. He no longer dreaded the future, nor the past, nor anything that threatened to snatch his peace away.

No, no condition was permanent. Or else he would still be under his aunt's heavy arm. Something really puzzled him about his aunt. He turned to see if Ama was ready for the question that popped into his mind.

Her face was calm, but she was clearly engrossed in her own thoughts. He decided not to interrupt her. In any case he did not know how Ama would feel if he were to start discussing Goma with her. The years had eventually broken those mother-and-daughter ties between his aunt and Ama, as the girl grew to love her new home and people. But he thought it better not to mention the subject. This evening was too nice to spoil.

He shelved his own thoughts. It was not important, but he was puzzled all the same. How did his aunt survive the illness that everyone thought would kill her? Tough as steel, she had not only survived the sickness but had come through the traumatic experience of having a 'daughter' and a nephew snatched from her. Adu had paid her a number of visits, but his most cherished memory was of the day he openly confessed his bitterness against her and asked her forgiveness.

Adu turned his mind to Ama. Yes, she did deserve her own apartment. She was a grown woman now. She had completed a secretarial course in Abenase, their home town, and settled down to work as a secretary at the Ministry of Health.

'I like the way you type!' Adu suddenly remarked. Ama laughed. How did this connect with their conversation?

Suddenly Adu felt this was the moment he had been waiting for. He was twenty-five and ready for marriage. And whenever he thought of it no woman came to his mind but Ama. They shared the same faith and a similar past. They had prayed together, cried together, shared moments of deep concern, and encouraged one another. Ama was the woman for him.

He picked his words carefully. 'Listen, Ama. I'm looking into the future, and us living together as husband and wife. That's what I've been wanting to tell you—to find out from you... You said you wanted to have your own flat. And I'm asking you to come and join me! The reason I asked you for this walk was so that I could ask you to marry me. I love you, and I know you know it.'

She did know it. She had known Adu would bring up the subject soon but not this evening. Some of her friends at the hospital had asked her if she had any man in mind. She always said yes. That kept the men away. Now there was no need to pretend or hide. Adu was her man.

She stopped. Adu turned to her with a question on his lips. But he had no time to ask it. Ama said, 'I love you, Adu. Very much.'

They stood face to face, in the middle of the lane. Their shining eyes told the story of their longing for each other. Impulsively Adu hugged Ama as tightly as he could. He kissed her and she kissed him. They knew that they belonged to one another.

More fiction from Lion Publishing:

THE BREAKING OF EZRA RILEY

John L. Moore

'You can only kick a dog so much before it becomes mean.' Pearl Riley saw it happening to her son, Ezra.

Faced with a respected but aloof father, ridiculing uncles, and the harsh cowboy environment of eastern Montana, eighteen-year-old Ezra finally flees from the family ranch. But seven years later, after his father's death, something pulls him back with his wife and young son to face the fears, challenges and enemies he had tried to escape.

Every obstacle will block his path as he struggles to maintain the ranch: drought, harsh winters, unforgiving relatives, death. But his ultimate encounter will be with himself.

The Breaking of Ezra Riley spans fifty years and three generations in a story of fathers, sons, and the land.

ISBN 0 7459 1882 4

CANDLE IN THE STRAW

Clare Wyatt

A compelling story of one woman, one family—
love, faith, courage—set in the turmoil and
revolution of China.

'Down with the traitors! Down with the enemies of
the People's Republic!'
In the midst of the hubbub Ling An walked in
silence. When they came to the field at the end of the
road they were halted and made to kneel in a long
row, their hands still bound together behind their
backs. The order was given to fire, yet Ling An
scarcely heard it. The sky above her was dark and
heavy, but glory surely lay beyond.

Clare Wyatt's compelling story is set in rural China.
It begins at the time of the Boxer Rebellion and ends
in the violence of the communist revolution.
Against this restless background the family saga
unfolds focused on the love, faith and courage of one
woman—Ling An.

ISBN 0 7459 1833 6

SONS AND BROTHERS

Elizabeth Gibson

*By faith and sword divided—a family saga set against
the background of the English Civil War*

'The buff and red coats merged, crossed and
separated. Which was the enemy? Robert paused,
half knowing the danger he was in, half denying it,
and steadied himself on a doorpost.

   'Then out of the rabble stepped a Goliath of a
man, or so it seemed. The man had lost his hat, but
the thick, black curls waving onto his broad
shoulders proclaimed him unmistakably a King's
man. Around them both the rain fell in black
curtains.

   'Suddenly he knew the other man...'

The agony of the nation is mirrored by the
brothers—Robert, the hard-line Puritan, Isaac the
King's man—divided by love and hate and warring
faiths. Passion and tragedy alternate in this richly
textured novel of two families, as King and
Parliament battle for supremacy.

ISBN 0 7459 1525 6

Not available from Lion Publishing in the USA

OLD PHOTOGRAPHS

Elizabeth Gibson

Christmas 1962: Bedford, Massachusetts.

Margaret with Ellie and her brother Don.

The first photograph...

From that moment Maggie loved him. From that
moment too she was bound to the McEnroe family:
    Ellie—beautiful, outrageous, self-destructive;
    Don—independent, stubborn, wedded to
farming;
    and Julius, their lawyer father—wealthy,
powerful, manipulative.

For Maggie, the decade of Woodstock and Vietnam
marks the start of a search for reality and the
meaning of love. Only the old photographs keep
hope alive as she waits with single-minded loyalty
for the only man she will ever love.

ISBN 0 7459 1855 7

HERE TO STAY

The four short stories in this book, all by women
with West Indian roots living in Britain, highlight
significant aspects of the black experience today.
Each takes the reader inside the situation, to feel and
understand.

Island roots are strong. Memories throw long
shadows. Who can find a place to stand between two
cultures?
   The black church is a tower of strength, a place of
shelter and community. Can a new generation keep
faith as they search for a way forward?
   Parents and children, bound by strong cords of
love, clash in the fight for freedom.
   How can the pain of continuing racial
discrimination be channelled for a constructive
future?

ISBN 0 7459 1829 8

Not available in USA